BORN UNIQUE
YOUR ENERGY BLUEPRINT

Activity Book based on Human Design

Chart showing Gates and Circuits

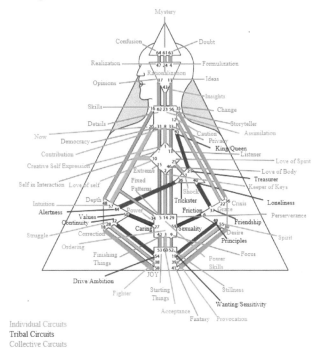

Individual Circuits
Tribal Circuits
Collective Circuits

Denise Reichmuth

Uncover Your Design
A step by step interactive guidebook based on your Human Design Chart
Foreword by Karen Curry Parker
Edited by Heather M Hillard

An Imprint for GracePoint Publishing, a division of its parent company:

www.GracePointPublishing.com
Permissions: 322 N Tejon St. #207 Colorado Springs CO 80903
www.GracePointMatrix.com Email: Admin@GracePointMatrix.com
SAN # 991-6032

ISBN-13: (Paperback) # 978-1-951694-12-8
eISBN: (eBook) # 978-1-951694-13-5

Books may be purchased for educational, business, or sales promotional use.
For bulk order requests and price schedule contact:
Orders@GracePointPublishing.com

Printed in the United States of America

SECTION ONE – Welcome to the World of Human Design

SECTION TWO – Type and Strategy

SECTION THREE – Centers

SECTION FOUR - Profiles

SECTION FIVE - Authority

SECTION SIX - Gates

Where does your path lead you?

Glossary

Authority: Defined Center that supports you in making decisions.

Center: Energy centers usually shown as triangle and square shapes on the Chart.

Channel: Created when two opposite Gates are defined and gives definition to the Centers at each end.

Chart: The graphic overview (map) showing your energetic blueprint.

Circuit: Group of channels that create a certain theme together: Individual, Collective or Tribal.

Conditioning: Energy and influences we have taken in due to our Openness and amplified.

Defined: Centers and Gates that are colored in and from where energy is 'broadcast out'.

Design: Your unconscious energetic imprint from 3 months before birth (shown in red).

Gate: The numbers shown in the Centers, representing the 64 archetypal themes of the Human blueprint and are based on the IChing system.

Incarnation Cross: Conscious and unconscious Sun and Earth Gate positions at birth.

Keynote: The generalization of compressing information into a single word or phrase.

Glossary

Line: Each Gate has six lines derived from the six lines of the IChing hexagram.

Monopole: Attracting (magnetic) force (one pole) that comes from the G-Center (Gate 2).

Motor: The defined Center(s) in the chart that provides extra energy.

Open: Undefined (white color) Centers and Gates - places that take in energy ('receiver') and where we have been conditioned by other people's energy.

Personality: Your conscious energetic imprinting at birth (shown in black).

Planet: As defined in Astrology, planets have an energetic theme and pass through different Gates at different speeds during the year.

Profile: The lines of the gates that conscious and unconscious Sun and Earth are located in at time of birth.

Strategy: Way to best decide and take action that is aligned with your natural energy flow according to your Type.

Themes: The archetypal energy of each gate

Type: Energy Field (Aura) defines the Type. Sacral Center is either defined or open.

Undefined: Open (white color) Centers and Gates - places that take in energy ('receiver').

Section One

Welcome to the World of Human Design

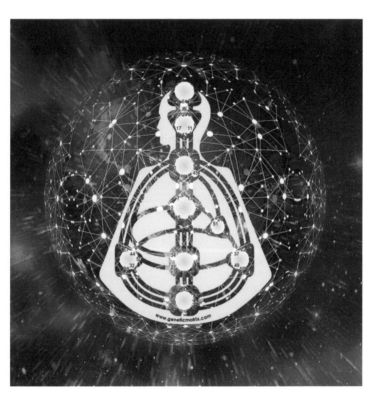

FOREWORD BY KAREN CURRY PARKER

HUMAN DESIGN IS A COMPLEX SYSTEM THAT CONTAINS ANCIENT AND MODERN CROSS-CULTURAL archetypes, mixed in with ancient and modern esoteric systems that can cause the average person a severe case of confusion and overwhelm, when they first receive their personal Human Design charts.

The complexity of Human Design can often turn people off. The amount of information, the interplay between the different parts of the chart and the alien vocabulary can make this highly accurate and potentially transformative system, inaccessible to many.

Despite the many "moving parts" in the Human Design chart, at its root, the system is simple. Memorizing all the parts of the chart, referencing them back to the various books and teachings about Human Design and creating your own understanding of your chart has been a task that is both time-consuming and frustrating for most people who first encounter their Human Design chart.

Even professional students struggle with the sheer volume of content in the system, often spending years trying to keep it all sorted out until enough "critical mass" of understanding is cultivated and integrated.

Up until now, there's never been an easy to use learning tool to help people take the information in their Human Design chart and make it accessible and relevant. In Discover Your Design, Denise Reichmuth has done what no one else has been able to; to make an easy to use, systematic study guide to help you learn your Human Design.

When you understand Human Design, a few about learning become obvious. First, most people are not designed to memorize or remember large quantities of information.

Secondly, people learn in many ways and most of us need a highly interactive way of learning for us to integrate information and really be able to recall and use it.

Thirdly, most of us can't learn if the process of learning isn't fun and enjoyable.

This workbook contains a simple way for you to interact and play with the information in the Human Design System so that it become relevant and easy for you to understand, learn and use.

There are many fantastic Human Design teachers in the world, each with their own spin and understanding of this amazingly accurate system. Students of Human Design often struggle to find ways to bridge the different teachings and to define their own synthesis of the vast amounts of information available.

Denise has carefully curated a beautiful collection of Human Design knowledge and created an inclusive and relevant way for people to deepen their own knowledge about their own charts and a way for professional students to quickly master the components of the Human Design System.

For years, my students have been asking for a study guide that would help them, not only understand Human Design, but support them in integrating all the information in the system. Denise has created the perfect tool to help people really integrate the teachings of Human Design. Denise has created the perfect learning tool!

Human Design teaches us that the world is changing quickly.

Our planet is demanding of us that we create in a sustainable way. But we cannot create sustainably if we ourselves are not sustainable.

Living true to who you really are is the fastest and most assured way to create alignment, authenticity and, ultimately, sustainability. Knowing your Human Design helps you shorten the self-discovery process and gives you concrete information to help you live a truly meaningful, purposeful life rooted in well-being.

Using this workbook to deepen your understanding of your personal Human Design and as a tool to help you understand not only yourself, but those you love, will help you fall in love with yourself and learn to create with great love and acceptance for others.

Not only that, when you live true to who you are - when you understand your Human Design - you learn to live life as yourself, to shed years of trying to be someone you're not and you truly fall in love with yourself.

And loving yourself is, I believe, the single most important thing you need to do to stay resilient in times of massive change!

Here's to your journey of self-discovery!

Karen Curry Parker

INTRODUCTION

ARE YOU PREPARED TO BE PART OF A LIVING EXPERIMENT? HUMAN DESIGN IS A MAP OF YOUR energy (energetic blueprint) and considered as an important personal development tool that helps you to see how unique you really are.

Ra Uru Hu (alias Alan (Robert) Krakower, 1948-2011) brought Human Design to the world and for over 25 years he taught this work on the energy dynamics and mechanics of what it means to be a human being. Ra received the information during a Supernova in 1987 while he was living the hermit life on the island of Ibiza. Ra was a 5/1 splenic Manifestor, originally from Canada and a musician and teacher. He was married and had children. His original videos on Human Design (in English) are available from Jovian Archive.

Human Design has made me more aware that each person has unique talents and capabilities that should be cherished and nurtured. This insight should encourage us to value our uniqueness (and not always compare ourselves to others). Each person has a unique theme to experience in this lifetime, so it's not an 'If I can do it - so can you' mentality with which we are confronted. In fact, the more you discover your own unique Human Design, the more you realize that you have your OWN (unique to you) way of being and doing things. Human Design helps you to become aware of the themes and characteristics you have brought with you into this life.

After Human Design came into my own life, I started to realize for the first time how unique each person truly is and to really understand that I also have my own unique-to-me themes and challenges in my life. The energy design is one part of awareness and the conditioning from our environment is the other part.

Human Design shows us that each person has a unique energy blueprint. This means each and every person has an influence on others and other people influence us, too, with their own energy and through the energy field.

Quantum physics shows us that all matter is energy, so the planets and our environment also play a role. We are literally energetically interacting with everything and everyone around us.

Human Design helps us become aware of the signals (energy) we are broadcasting as well as receiving and what our main theme or purpose is in life. It also shows us that there are different energy types in addition to the ideal way each type should interact with each other.

Challenges exist to help us grow and evolve. If we get stuck, this can feel like struggling or suffering; however, rest assured that suffering is not a theme in the Human Design Chart!

Human Design shows us what themes and characteristics were activated at the time of our birth. This is our energetic blueprint (map of how our energy flows) and the design always stays the same in this lifetime.

The themes have a wide spectrum in regards of how they are lived, i.e. they can be lived through high expression (expressed), not lived at all (repressed), or somewhere in-between. Human Design charts show the themes and highest possible expression, but not how the person is living out that theme in their life now. Only you can tell how you are expressing your themes or conditioning right now and decide whether you want to change something.

Human Design can be quite complex, the deeper you go into the topic. *The key takeaway here above all else is to just live according your Type and Strategy.* Then, you will be living in your correct energetic flow with the Universe. Just watch and observe what unfolds when you are living according to your strategy.

Imagine that the more people who know their Human Design type, the more choice they have when they recognize their uniqueness; these people decide to optimize how they interact with each other. This makes it clear that nothing is really personal - it is just the way we are designed and our choice whether to take things personally or not.

With this knowledge, people can interact with more conscious awareness — parents, teachers, and coaches to name a few — and even children will find this to be a valuable asset.

The motivation for putting this book together is to give a general foundation to which you can relate to and help Human Design to become more well known. The material in this book is in keynote style and more for quick reference than what I would call detailed learning. I hope all levels of Human Design students (or just people interested in this topic) will find this book helpful. I have also used more everyday vocabulary, which I find easier to understand, so this might also differ from some other Human Design material already available.

HOW TO USE THIS BOOK

To use this activity book, you will first need to first have your Human Design Chart calculated. In order to generate your Chart, the following information is needed:
- Date of birth
- Place of birth
- Time of birth

You can get your Chart in the following ways:
1. From a Human Design Specialist in person or via their website.
2. Internet (paid or free charts are available).
3. Download a Human Design App

I like to use: www.freehumandesignchart.com

This book is designed to introduce you to the concepts of Human Design (HD) with activities and brief explanations of how to interpret and understand your HD chart.

Each section has at least one activity page to complete (text or coloring in) based on your Human Design Chart. Responding to questions, or personalizing and coloring your chart helps anchor the information into your consciousness.

I recommend that you have a **red** and **black** pen or pencil available to color the blank charts as directed in the exercise.

Please bear in mind that the text content in this book is designed to give you an overview of the topic for simple understanding. For more in-depth information, please do your own research and use other resources

Have Fun Discovering Your Design!

Remember:
Live according to your Type and Strategy once you know what they are!

Curious to learn more? Let's dive in!

WHAT IS HUMAN DESIGN?

Human Design:

- IS LIKE A ROLODEX OF HUMAN ARCHETYPES WITH ACCOMPANYING THEMES (KNOWN AS YOUR life purpose).
- shows how mechanisms work on an energetic level.
- shows us that an energy blueprint is activated at birth with thematic activations that may be expressed in various ways - or not at all (repressed).
- is shown as a Chart or in a Mandala Wheel

HUMAN DESIGN CHART

- Shows **Design** and **Personality** activation

- Has 9 centers (based on the Hindu Chakra System)

- Has 3 major circuit groups and 7 subcircuits

- Shows the planetary influences

- Uses the 64 hexagrams (Gates) of the I'Ching

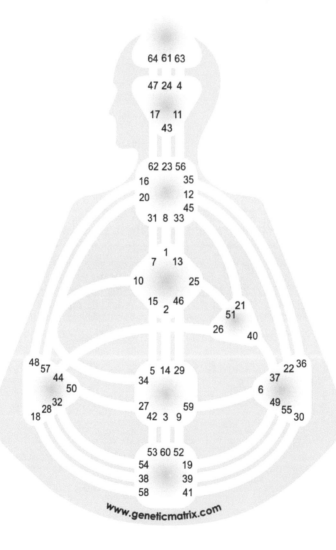

www.geneticmatrix.com

DESIGN and PERSONALITY

THE PLANETARY POSITIONS AT THE TIME OF BIRTH ACTIVATE YOUR ENERGY BLUEPRINT. THIS IS always the foundational energy that is active in this lifetime.

At the time of birth, your Personality is also created, i.e. the black numbers (Gates) are activated and delineated on your Chart. This is the part we call the mind; it is supposed to be like the passenger in the car and <u>witness</u> what is occurring (it is not supposed to drive the car).

88 degrees astrologically (which is about three months before birth), your Design is established, i.e. the red numbers (Gates) are activated and defined on your Chart. This is the part we call physical body intelligence or the vehicle that is carrying us through life.

So **Design** and **Personality** activations together create your Human Design Chart.

> **It is important to remember EVERYONE HAS ALL OF THE ENERGIES IN THE CHART** <u>available</u>.

We can all feel and relate to all of the energies that are shown in the Chart. The activations we have are the energies to which we have more consistent access and so they seem more dominant in our life.

HUMAN DESIGN FULL CHART - EXAMPLE

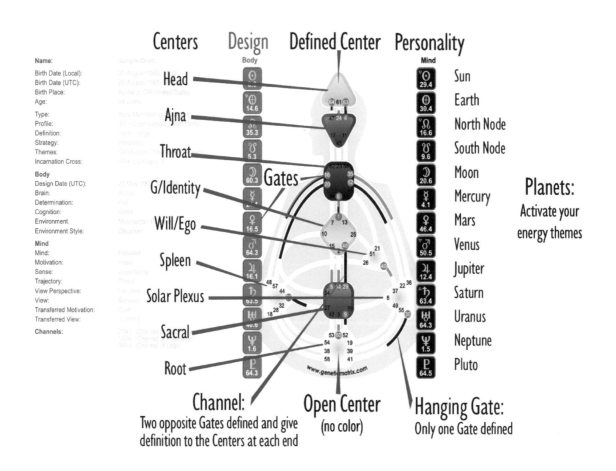

Centers — **Design** (Body) — **Defined Center** — **Personality** (Mind)

Head
Ajna
Throat — Gates
G/Identity
Will/Ego
Spleen
Solar Plexus
Sacral
Root

Planets: Activate your energy themes

Sun
Earth
North Node
South Node
Moon
Mercury
Mars
Venus
Jupiter
Saturn
Uranus
Neptune
Pluto

Name:
Birth Date (Local):
Birth Date (UTC):
Birth Place:
Age:

Type:
Profile:
Definition:
Strategy:
Themes:
Incarnation Cross:

Body
Design Date (UTC):
Brain:
Determination:
Cognition:
Environment:
Environment Style:

Mind
Mind:
Motivation:
Sense:
Trajectory:
View Perspective:
View:
Transferred Motivation:
Transferred View:

Channels:

Channel:
Two opposite Gates defined and give definition to the Centers at each end

Open Center
(no color)

Hanging Gate:
Only one Gate defined

www.geneticmatrix.com

HUMAN DESIGN MANDALA - EXAMPLE

Shows the location of the planets at time of birth

Gate Numbers
Gate 41 is the beginning of the Human Design year (progressing counter clockwise around the mandala).

Planet Earth
(Position is always opposite the Sun).

Astrological Wheel

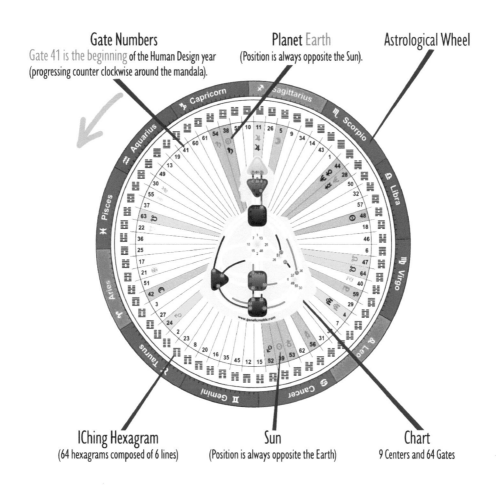

IChing Hexagram
(64 hexagrams composed of 6 lines)

Sun
(Position is always opposite the Earth)

Chart
9 Centers and 64 Gates

Section Two

Type and Strategy

Look at your **Human Design Chart** and write down your
Type and **Strategy** here:

1) My **TYPE:**

_____

2) My **STRATEGY** (for decision making):

_____

3) How does my **TYPE** want to be asked?
   - ☐   Open ended questions
   - ☐   Yes/No questions

4) Does my **TYPE** have sustainable energy?
   (Is the Sacral Center defined?)
   - ☐   Yes
   - ☐   No

ADDITIONAL NOTES:

_____
_____
_____

EXPLANATION of the 5 TYPES and STRATEGIES

HUMAN DESIGN DEFINES 5 ENERGY TYPES. THE TYPE IS DETERMINED BY THE ENERGY FIELD AROUND the body (aura) and whether they are energy (Sacral Center defined) or non-energy Types. Each Type has a Strategy, meaning the way they best make their decisions. Type and Strategy are usually shown on the Human Design Chart.

Some Human Design material defines only 4 energy types. The 5th energy type is the Manifesting Generator - a combination of Manifestor and Generator types. The Manifesting Generator is considered a Generator type.

Energy Types	% of Population	Also Known As:
MANIFESTOR	8%	INITIATOR
MANIFESTING GENERATOR	33%	EXPRESS BUILDER
GENERATOR	37%	CLASSIC BUILDER
PROJECTOR	21%	ADVISOR or COORDINATOR
REFLECTOR	1%	EVALUATOR

We live in a Generator Type world (70% of the population). Generator Types represent the majority of the population, so dominate our environment through their behavior. Human Design helps people to better understand themselves as well as others and clearly shows us that each energy Type is different.

The Centers and Gates also influence how you express and live out your energy Type. All the elements of the Chart play together. Note that these are all themes that are expressed through each unique person and whatever gets expressed is not (usually) supposed to be taken personally.

The following overview shows how the different energy Types flow together as a team so that humanity can evolve, grow, and manifest their ideas together.

The Manifestor has the ideas and initiates (gets the ball rolling/motivates others). The Generator Type brings the ideas into form and does the work needed while Projectors see the whole picture and are here to guide and advise (also help to anchor and stabilize the energies of and on the Earth). The Reflectors reflect the overall health of the community where they live or serve, acting like an early indicator for others similar to how a canary lets workers know if there's too little oxygen to stay in a coal mine.

All Types *except* the Reflector are solar beings (attuned to the 365-day cycle of the earth around the sun). Solar beings are primarily affected by the transit of the sun during the year in addition to other planetary influences.

The Reflector is a lunar being (attuned to the 28-day cycle of the moon around the earth). Reflectors are primarily affected by a different energy each day during the 28-day cycle of the moon transit in addition to other planetary influences. So they need to wait a lunar cycle of 28-day before making any decisions.

MANIFESTOR

Strategy (decision making)

 Obey and follow their creative flow; inform those beings impacted by their decisions. (Others should also inform them of any decisions that may affect them.)

Only energy type that can initiate things without waiting to respond to external stimuli.

Have no sustainable life energy from the sacral center. Need to pay attention to how they use their energy. A conventional working model is difficult for this Type.

Solar Being (365-day cycle).

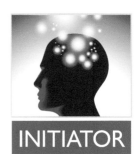

INITIATOR

Ask Open Ended Questions

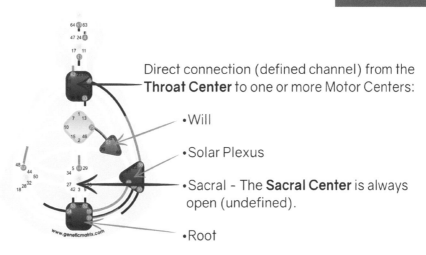

Direct connection (defined channel) from the **Throat Center** to one or more Motor Centers:

- Will

- Solar Plexus

- Sacral - The **Sacral Center** is always open (undefined).

- Root

Non-energy Type

 Emotional themes:

Anger - Peace.
May need support to manage anger

Does not like to be disturbed in their inner creative flow as they lose their train of thought and then can appear angry.

GOOD TO KNOW

- Works well alone
- Likes being alone
- Does not like feeling controlled by others or told what to do
- Needs to feel free
- Informing others is important, but not always welcomed by those impacted.

Aura (energy field around the body)

Feels like a closed, almost repelling energy that may make others feel you are unapproachable. Does not feel very inviting.

It is advisable to teach children to get used to informing those around them. Manifestor children are designed to follow their ideas and so easily forget to inform others of what action they are planning to take. For example: A child leaves the house (without informing anybody) and goes to the park, following their train of thought. Note: They are not deliberately misbehaving or being naughty.

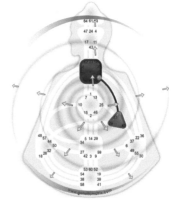

MANIFESTOR

MANIFESTING GENERATOR

Strategy (decision making)

 Wait and respond to Sacral response to external things.

Are first and foremost Generator Types; often respond with a guttural sound : 'Uh-huh (yes) / 'uh-uh' (no).

Secondary: Can initiate and act on the ideas they have (like the Manifestor Types).

The original true Manifesting Generator has the Sacral Center directly connected to the Throat Center through the defined channel 34-20. This defined channel makes them very fast in thought and action; it even takes too long for them to express the sounds of 'uh-huh (yes) or uh-uh' (no).

 Solar Being (365-day cycle).

FAST & BUSY

Ask Yes/No Questions

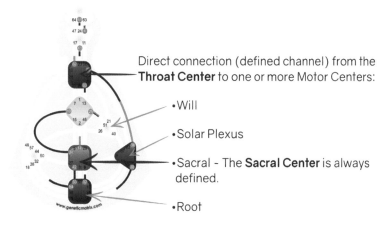

Direct connection (defined channel) from the **Throat Center** to one or more Motor Centers:

- Will
- Solar Plexus
- Sacral - The **Sacral Center** is always defined.
- Root

Energy Type

 Emotional themes:

Frustration - Satisfaction.
May need support to manage anger

Appear to get things done quicker than Generator Types, but they like to skip steps in between and have to go back later.

Physical movement is important.

Aura (energy field around the body)

Is open and enveloping. Others feel they have a curtain around them. It is not personal.

They 'throw spaghetti' against the wall to see what 'sticks'. They need to experiment to see what works. It's OK when everything is not successful!

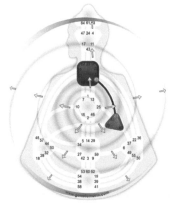

MANIFESTOR

GENERATOR

Strategy (decision making)

 Wait and respond to Sacral Center response to external things (not ideas in their head).
Sustainable lifeforce energy to do what they love. Sacral response usually expressed through sound: 'uh-huh' (yes) or 'uh-uh' (no).

 Solar beings (365-day cycle).

Wait to respond

Ask Yes/No Questions

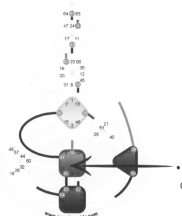

•Sacral - The **Sacral Center** is always defined.

Energy Type

 Emotional themes:

Frustration - Satisfaction.

Moving forward step by step with phases of frustration in between (when nothing seems to move). This is when the next new opportunity is being created.

It is helpful to be physically active.

Aura (energy field around the body)

Seems open and envelopping.
Others feel like they have a curtain around them. It is not personal.

Remember to give yourself time for clarity if your Solar Plexus center is defined.

Something to ponder:
If your Sacral Center energy was a sum of money, would you think first about how to best use this money?

GENERATOR

PROJECTOR

Strategy (decision making)

 Wait for the invitation or to be asked

Access to constant lifeforce energy is missing with an open Sacral Center. So it is important that they pay attention to how they manage and use their energy. The conventional working model is difficult for non-energy types.

Are here to learn about themselves through others.

They guide and advise'their tribe'.

 Solar beings (365-day cycle).

Wait for invitation

Ask open ended questions

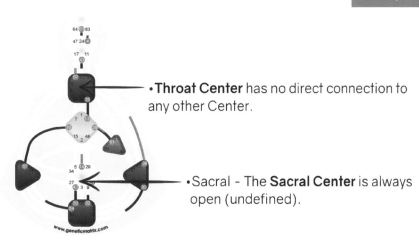

• **Throat Center** has no direct connection to any other Center.

• Sacral - The **Sacral Center** is always open (undefined).

www.geneticmatrix.com

Non-energy Type

 Emotional themes:

Bitterness – Success.

Help anchoring energies on the earth.

Best to let things pass through and not hold on to them. It's not personal. Be a screen - not a sponge.

Aura (energy field around the body)

Focused on one person/thing.

Can feel like a hand that penetrates to the heart (G-Center). Penetrates through the aura of others - can feel uncomfortable.

Note: Children at school can seem reserved. Praise and recognition are important. Projectors need others to listen to them without necessarily giving advice as they gain clarity through speaking out loud. Ask them for advice and give them the appropriate praise and recognition.

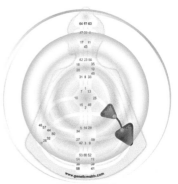

PROJECTOR

REFLECTOR

Strategy (decision making)

 Wait a 28-day lunar cycle to gain clarity
Access to constant lifeforce energy is missing with an open Sacral Center. So it is important that they pay attention how they manage and use their energy. The conventional working model is difficult for non-energy types.

Need time to be alone in their own energy (not being influenced by others) to evaluate and gain clarity — and also to regenerate.

 Lunar beings (28-day lunar cycle).

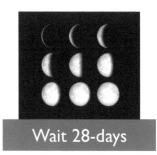

Wait 28-days

Ask open ended questions

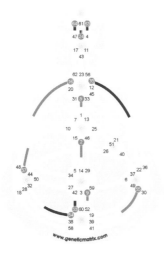

All 9 Centers are open (undefined).

Non-energy Type

Emotional themes:

Disappointment - Surprise.

Are like a barometer - the canary in the coal mine. Reflect the overall energetic health of their communities. Are highly sensitive to what is happening around them.

Are empathic - feel the energies of others.

Aura (energy field around the body)

Sample along the edge of the aura of others and feel if all are in harmony with the energetic field.

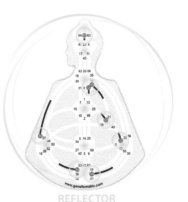

REFLECTOR

Can feel like resistance. Repels energy that is not healthy or conductive to their experience (teflon effect).

When they are happy and doing well, they are in the right place.

TYPES OVERVIEW

MANIFESTOR 8% INITIATOR		Sacral Center open Throat Center directly connected to a 'motor'	 Obey and follow the inner creative flow.
MANIFESTING GENERATOR 33% TIME BENDER		Sacral defined 'uh-huh / uh-uh'	 Wait and respond to something external.
GENERATOR 37% ALCHEMIST			
PROJECTOR 21% ORCHESTRATOR		Sacral Center open	 Wait for the invitation or to be asked.
REFLECTOR 1% CALIBRATOR		All 9 Centers open	 Wait a 28-day lunar cycle.

Do you always act according to your TYPE and STRATEGY?

 Be informed and inform others impacted.

- Works best alone
- Aura: Repelling

ANGER
PEACE

 What sticks?

- Works best in groups
- Aura: Enveloping

FRUSTRATION
SATISFACTION

 Stair-step forward.

 Be a screen - not a sponge!

- Works best one-on-one
- Aura: Penetrating

BITTERNESS
SUCCESS

 Barometer.

- Works best as part of a group but not alone
- Aura: Sampling

DISAPPOINT
SURPRISE

Section Three
Centers

Look at your **Human Design chart** and write down the information on the following pages:

1) How many Centers are defined (colored in) on the Human Design chart?

_____

2) Write down the name(s) of the **Defined Centers**:

_____

_____

_____

3) How many Centers are open (white) on the **Human Design chart**?

_____

4) Write down the name of the open (white) **Centers**:

_____

_____

_____

On the image below color in the **CENTERS** that are defined (colored in) on your
HUMAN DESIGN CHART.

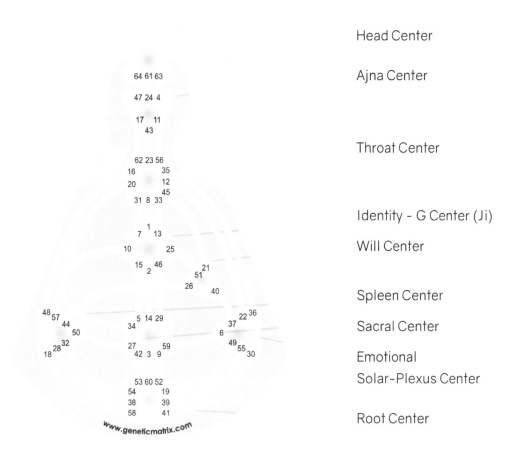

Head Center

Ajna Center

Throat Center

Identity - G Center (Ji)

Will Center

Spleen Center

Sacral Center

Emotional
Solar-Plexus Center

Root Center

Defined Sacral Center are always Generator Types i.e. Manifesting Generator or Generator

Open (undefined) Sacral Center are the other Types i.e. Manifestor, Projector oder Reflector.

DEFINED

64 61 63

The colored Centers (shapes) are called DEFINED Centers. They **broadcast energy out** and you are **consciously** aware of it. The energy experienced here is rather fixed and consistent no matter what other energies are around you (people, animals, plants, etc.)

ANALOGY: You have only a fixed menu to choose options in a restaurant. So your **choice is limited, but consistent.**

OPEN (undefined)

64 61 63

The white centers are called UNDEFINED (or OPEN) Centers. These Centers are like **receiving channels** and you are **not consciously** aware of inbound energies. The energy experienced here is variable (meaning not constant like defined Centers).

ANALOGY: You have a all-you-can-eat buffet available in a restaurant. So you have a **variety of choices** and variability.

The energy here is variable and also amplifies the energy of others with defined Centers.

HEAD CENTER

Seat of the Personality Crystal.

The head wants to know:
- How?
- What if?
- Can this be true?

The mind has two roles:
- Stimulate a specific vibrational energy
- Process data

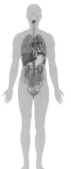

ANATOMY:
Associated with the pineal gland in the bra

DEFINED: **30% of the POPULATION**

Feel under pressure to find an answer.

HOW?

Designed to imagine and dream about possibilities - not to figure things out or make decisions!

Designed to be inspired (by the Root Center) and use imagination of Head Center which triggers feelings (in Solar Plexus Center).

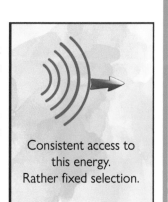

Consistent access to this energy.
Rather fixed selection.

'Passenger'

Look at your **Human Design Chart** and color the Head Center below if it is defined (colored) on your chart.

64 61 63

OPEN: **70% of the POPULATION**

Feel under pressure to figure out the answers to other people's questions (taken in unconsciously).

Are wise about ideas and beliefs - do not just adopt them!

Always feel inspired. Best to stay in state of wonder. Only take action if it is according to your strategy!

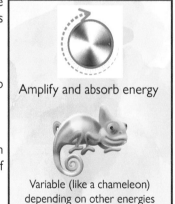

Amplify and absorb energy

Variable (like a chameleon) depending on other energies around them

AJNA CENTER

Seat of the
Design **Crystal.**

Anatomy:
- Associated with
- anterior and posterior
- pituitary glands.

'Vehicle'

DEFINED: **30% of the POPULATION**

Stores concepts, beliefs, thoughts. Is certain. Can hold on to ideas and information with certainty.

Fixed in how it works but reliable and trustworthy.

Remember that others may see the information differently.

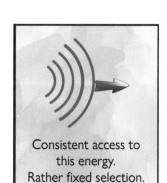

Consistent access to this energy.
Rather fixed selection.

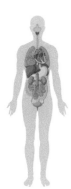

ANATOMY:

Associated with anterior and posterior pituitary glands.

Look at your **Human Design Chart** and color the Ajna Center below if it is defined (colored) on your chart.

47 24 4

17   11

43

OPEN:

70% of the POPULATION

Visualizing is difficult for many. Open Ajna is not designed to visualize.

Designed to be in the flow of ideas. Not designed to be certain or hold onto ideas and beliefs or remember data.

See many sides of an issue.

Write down what you want to remember. Can be very intellectual. Is difficult to be certain (often told to make up your mind.)

Amplify and absorb energy

Variable depending on other energies around them

THROAT CENTER

Anatomy:
- Master Gland Center
- Thyroid and Parathyroid

All energies want to get to the Throat Center

DEFINED: 70% of the POPULATION

Designed to speak (about whatever Gate themes are activated.).

Communicates easily when Throat Center is motorized (connected to a Motor Center: Root, Sacral, Solar Plexus, Will).

Use your Strategy according to your Types before speaking.

Speak carefully and responsibly. Words are a powerful energy.

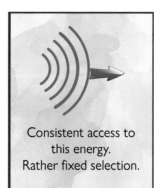

Consistent access to this energy.
Rather fixed selection.

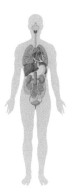

ANATOMY:
Master Gland Center,
Thyroid and Parathyroid

Look at your **Human Design Chart** and color the Throat Center below if it is defined (colored) on your chart.

62 23 56

16   35

20   12

              45

31 8 33

OPEN: **30% of the POPULATION**

Not designed to speak a lot.

Are heard best through being silent (aura does the talking).

May struggle for recognition and being heard.

May feel under pressure to speak to release energy.

Wait to be recognized and asked.

It's easier to speak when someone with a Defined Throat Center is present.

Amplify and absorb energy

Variable depending on other energies around them

G-CENTER (JI) / IDENTITY (HEART)

1
7   13
10   25
15   46
2

Seat of the Soul. Center of
Love and Direction.

Your mind, will and emotions attune the vibration of your **G-Center** and the **Magnetic Monopole**, attracting things with the same vibration into your **personal reality**

Seat of the Magnetic Monopole
in Gate 2 "Driver"

DEFINED: **55% of the POPULATION**

Feel love and have Self-Love.

Here to give love and empower others.

Good sense of Self. Knows where the journey is going but not how.

Vulnerable to criticism when full channel connected to the Throat Center.

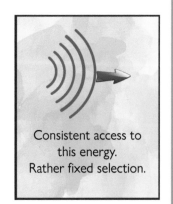

Consistent access to
this energy.
Rather fixed selection.

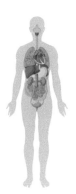

ANATOMY:
Liver

Look at your **Human Design Chart** and color the G-Center below if it is defined (colored) on your chart.

1
7 13
10   25
15   46
2

OPEN: 45% of the POPULATION

Are here to be wise through experiencing others.

Difficult for them to feel their own energy. Need to be aware that other's energy play a role. Can feel like own energy is being overridden.

Important that everything feels correct: Clothes (inside labels irritate), home environment and furnishings, geographical location, seating place, people and things around you.

May seem fussy and hard to please.

Don't feel comfortable when things are not correct for them.

Often question their lovability and Self-esteem.

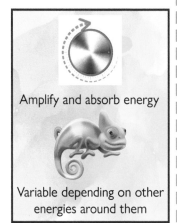

Amplify and absorb energy

Variable depending on other energies around them

ENERGETIC THEMES of the G-CENTER

THE G-CENTER (Identity Center) has Gates with the following characteristics, which are often considered as characteristics of the heart.

The highest potential for Love comes from our potential for Self-Love (Gate 10) and our own sense of Empowerment (Gate 7). We are here to BE Love.

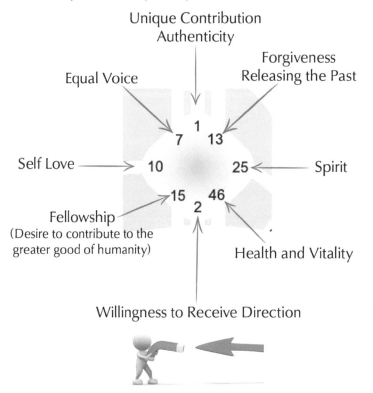

Seat of the Magnetic Monopole in Gate 2 – acts like a giant one-pole magnet **only attracting things to us that are a vibrational match.**

The Magnetic Monopole synchronizes with the 8 Themes (energies) of the G-Center and is also influenced by the Solar Plexus Center (emotional center).

MAGNETIC MONOPOLE

Holds the Design and Personality Crystals together in a relationship (not always in harmony).

Located in the G–Center (Sternum).

"Driver"

Is like our internal GPS-system: knows where we are in space and how to get us to our destination.

Only attracts things to us that are a vibrational match. Attracting force is called love.

Holds us in the illusion of separation and gives us our direction in life.

Guides us along our path (our 'Vehicle') with which we are in alignment when we use our Strategy and Authority correctly.

Called forth from the Earth with the Design-Crystal at time of conception.

According to Human Design the crystals are energetic Crystals of Consciousness (not physical crystals). All life forms have two Crystals.

Neutrinos are tiny particles carrying mass (i.e. information) and capable of leaving an imprint. They are produced by all living stars. Trillions of neutrinos (with information) pass through our entire planet - and us - every second and, therefore, have an effect on our energy as well as our world.

The neutrino stream is filtered through our Crystals of Consciousness.

OVERVIEW of the CRYSTALS of CONSCIOUSNESS

'Vehicle'
Physical Body
Yin Energy
Human Self
(Personal Self – Identity)

DESIGN CRYSTAL – LIFE PURPOSE

Holds the story of who you are in this life.

Life plan.

Imprinting in the womb at **88** degrees before the time of birth.

Design – red numbers (GATES) shown on your Human Design Chart.

Subconscious level – no consistent access to this information. Don't know what will emerge.

Holds the blueprint of current level of consciousness and conditioning on the planet at time of conception and synchronizes the development, maintenance and sustenance of your physical health and wellness.

Holds the plot outline for your Life Purpose and is like a suit you are wearing in this lifetime.

How you are genetically programmed to move through time in space.

Is in charge of the life together with the Magnetic Monopole.

Called forth from the Earth at the time of conception from father's energy together with the Magnetic Monopole.

> Ideally, we need to stay connected to our soul path to live our fully activated, aligned life. Alignment and

64

47

1

PERSONALITY CRYSTAL – SOUL PURPOSE

Intention of the soul in this life. Cosmic plan

Located above the head (scalp) in the Head Center.

Imprinting at time of birth.

Personality - black numbers (Gates) shown on your Human Design Chart.

Conscious access to this information.

Head and Ajna are connected through the pineal gland.

'Passenger'
Mind
Yang Energy
Cosmic Self
Unaware of the
Design Crystal

63

Holds the blueprint of the intention of your Soul (seeking to do, embody, and manifest) in this lifetime.

'Passenger' (mind) really has no control over the 'vehicle' (body) (although they may think they do). Best to just sit back and enjoy the ride!

Who you think you are.

Thinks it is in charge of the life. Conflicts often arise.

When the Neo-Cortex has fully developed the Personality Crystal emerges and enters your body at time of birth.

Connection comes through using Strategy and Authority correctly. We differentiate first and then unify.

WILL CENTER (EGO)

(also belongs to the heart
with G Center)

It is important to follow your Strategy – it could be lifesaving!

Willpower and Values

DEFINED: 35% (1/8) of the POPULATION

1 of the 4 'Motors'

Designed to work to rest
and need cycles of rest

Can push through and have endurance to get things done.

Always working and pushing with your will center will in time burn you out.

Overuse affects the cardiovascular system, stomach or thymus (auto immune disorders).

Can energetically empower others and make them feel they can do anything (whilst they are in your aura).

Consistent access to
this energy.
Rather fixed selection.

Important to keep any
promises made

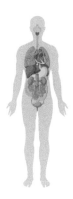

ANATOMY (Gates):
Heart (21),
Stomach (40),
Gallbladder (51),
Thymus (26)

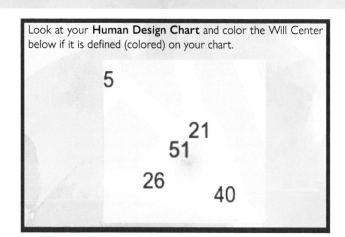

Look at your **Human Design Chart** and color the Will Center below if it is defined (colored) on your chart.

5

21
51
26
40

OPEN: ## 65% (7/8) of the POPULATION

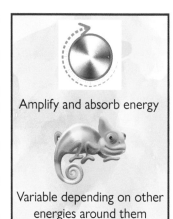

Need to prove their value. Struggle with value and self-worth.

Here to become wise about what is valuable in life.

We are taught to get things done and often force ourselves through will power, which can lead to burn out.

Common to undervalue self (i.e. not charging enough for your work)

Can be co-dependency trap if unaware of this energy.

Will maintain resources for the tribe and self.

Amplify and absorb energy

Variable depending on other energies around them

Do NOT
"Just Go Do It."

SPLEEN CENTER

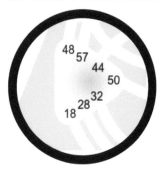

Immune System /Healing

Center for:
- Intuition
- Instinct
- Fear
- Timing
- Immune System
- /Healing

Intuition

DEFINED: ## 55% of the POPULATION

Good sense of time

Here to be wise about healing.

Immune system is not so sensitive - often do not notice when they are seriously ill.

Survival in the NOW. Impulse only comes once. Important to take action. Spontaneous.

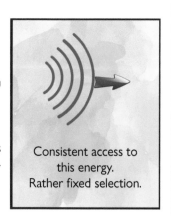

Consistent access to this energy.
Rather fixed selection.

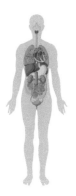

ANATOMY:
Spleen
Lymphatic System
Immune System

Look at your **Human Design Chart** and color the Spleen Center below if it is defined (colored) on your chart.

48 57
44
50
32
18 28

OPEN: 45% of the POPULATION

Fear gates live here. Fear in the now.

Fear of not being enough, not perfect.

Responsibility - can feel paralysing.

Children may feel fear of separation.

Push through the fears and do it anyway!

Like to be around people with a defined splenic center. Feels nourishing and strengthening.

People tend to hold on to things for longer than is good for them (can be fears or material things, old hurts, belongings, relationships).

Have a fluid sense of time. Timekeeping is a challenge. Are either too early or too late.

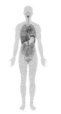

Can be good medical empaths

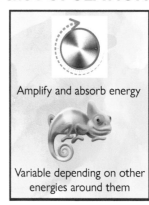

Amplify and absorb energy

Variable depending on other energies around them

SOLAR PLEXUS CENTER

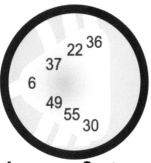

22 36
37
6
49 55 30

Immune System /Healing

Is the energy frequency that synchronizes the Magnetic Monopole (electro-magnetic attraction field of the heart)

1 of the 4 'Motors'

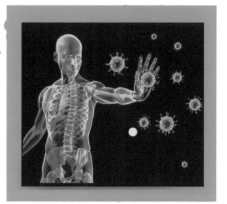

DEFINED:

I feel happy instead of I am happy.

Energy for creativity, passion, abundance.
Be aware of how long your cycle lasts so that you can wait a full cycle before making decisions. Energy has to feel right consistently throughout your wave.
Pay attention to regular 'low' wave cycles.
This is normal and is not necessarily a sign of depression!

50% of the POPULATION

Consistent access to this energy.
Rather fixed selection.

Waves: Channel 59-6 is wave source

Tribal
(19-49 + 37-40)
Physical touch + sensitive to needs. Builds up gradually till explodes. Creative expression.

Individual
(39-55 + 22-12)
‹In the mood› **Short ups and downs. Wait out the wave. Have alone time.**

Collective
(36-35 + 41-30)
Desire - feeling, Wave crashes when expectation not met. Don't make quick decisions!

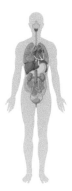

ANATOMY (Gates):
Kidneys
Pancreas

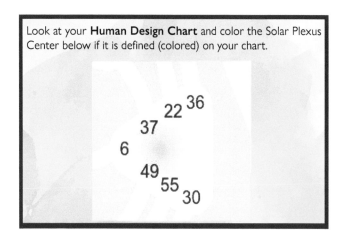

Look at your **Human Design Chart** and color the Solar Plexus Center below if it is defined (colored) on your chart.

22 36
37
6
49
55
30

OPEN:

Be a Screen – not a sponge!

Don't take things personally!

(Let the energy pass through) - (Don't hold on to the energy)

50% of the POPULATION

Do not like to 'rock the boat'. Harmony is important.

Feels the energy of the emotionally defined center and it can feel uncomfortable. Tends to want to keep everyone happy.

May avoid dealing with truth and conflict, especially if others are going to react.

Often compromise to avoid truth if it leads to conflict. Question if it is your energy.

Best to get out of the other person's auric field - especially important for children.

Sensitive to emotional environment. Emotional empaths.

Can be overwhelm, pain, confusion, sensitivity.

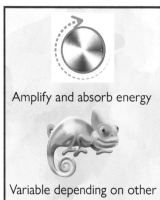

Amplify and absorb energy

Variable depending on other energies around them

Emotional Waves and the Defined Solar Plexus

When your Solar Plexus Center is defined then you have what is known as emotional waves. Depending which Gates or Channels are defined you may have one or all three wave types as shown below. When you notice these emotional waves it is important to allow yourself the time to feel your way through the wave - so wait for clarity and don't make decisions immediately. Those with an open Solar Plexus can feel and amplify these emotions (waves).

Tribal channel 59-6 energy is where the emotional wave starts to take form. Good to make physical contact whilst talking. Speaks through the aura.

Keep your baseline at a high level

What you focus on expands - waves fluctuate - so you can have good and bad days. So do you focus on the low or high part of the wave? The aim is to have a high quality, high frequency emotional wave. No variation is like a flatline (on a hospital monitor this means you're dead). So paying attenton to the quality of your baseline (overall height and frequency of your wave) helps.

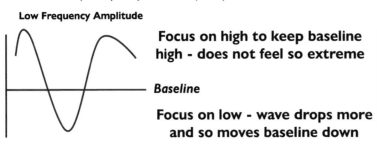

Focus on high to keep baseline high - does not feel so extreme

Baseline

Focus on low - wave drops more and so moves baseline down

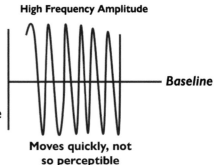

Tribal Wave

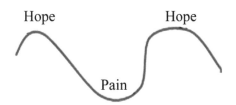

Channels 49-19 and 37-40 have emotional waves that are cyclical. It gets triggered in relationships - to do with the family, tribe or people they care about. This wave is usually not felt so much in daily experience.

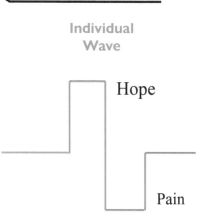

Individual Wave

Channels 39-55 and 22-12 have intense emotional waves that are expressed as emotional highs and lows (may seem melancholilc or depressed). About being in the mood and waiting out the wave cycle. The depth and height of wave is influenced by intention and attention. Can be very creative (music, poetry, all kinds of art). Physical movement helps to stabilize. When these channels get connected:

High internal auditory energy and knowing circuit - so know things and may struggle to articulate or explain things when energy doesn't get to the Throat Center. Need to make sure are well hydrated to shift vibration. Sometimes have sugar cravings.

Collective wave

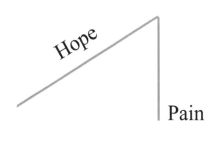

Channels 36-35 and 41-30 have emotional waves that build up and drop (crash) - so this wave does not have the same highs or lows as the individual wave. More to do with desire. Advisable to wait before making any decisions.

SACRAL CENTER

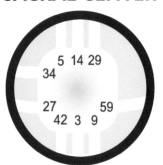

5 14 29
34

27   59
42 3 9

Burned out (tired) Will Center may affect the 'non-response' of the Sacral Center.

Reproductive organs (Ovaries und Testes)

1 of the 4 'Motors'

Physical exercise is important!

DEFINED: 70% of the POPULATION

Only Manifesting Generator and Generator Energy Types.

Sacral Response:

Practice giving a spontaneous guttural response to things in your environment (from outide, not inside your head):

'uh-huh' (instead of 'yes') or
'uh-uh' (instead of 'no')

and see how quickly you know and feel the answer to what is right for you. Need Yes/No questions to respond to.

Center for sustainable life force energy as long as they are doing what they love to do (correct for their energy). Recharge 'battery' overnight.

Sacral (gutteral) response shows *you* what is correct for **your** energy - it is NOT a mental decision.

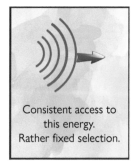

Consistent access to this energy. Rather fixed selection.

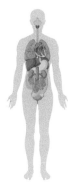

ANATOMY:

- Reproductive organs
- (Ovaries und Testes)

Look at your **Human Design Chart** and color the Sacral Center below if it is defined (colored) on your chart.

5 14 29
34

27   59
42 3 9

OPEN: ## 30% of the POPULATION

Projector, Manifestor, Reflector. Non-energy Types.

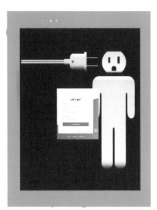

No sustainable energy of their own - not here to work in the traditional (generator) way. Sometimes perceived by others as being lazy.

Learn how to manage your energy in a way that is correct for you.

Give yourself alone time and time to rest to discharge excess sacral energy from your system.

Important to go to bed before you are sleepy!

Sometimes hard to tune into when enough is enough.

Consider sleeping alone in your own aura to regenerate effectively.

Amplify and absorb energy

Variable depending on other energies around them

ROOT CENTER

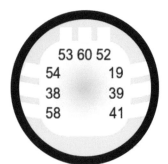

53 60 52
54 19
38 39
58 41

Is the center for adrenaline
Energy **and** 'Drive'

Inspiration comes from RootCenter. (Head Center uses imagination).

1 of the 4 'Motors'

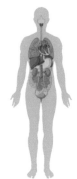

ANATOMY (Gates):
- Adrenal glands (abov the kidneys).
- Adrenaline productic

DEFINED: ## 50% of the POPULATION

ON-OFF Pulse
Also influences the Sacral Center response.

Operates in 'on/off' cycles or pulses depending on which gates are defined around this center. Take action when the pulse is on.
Has 'pulses' of focus and concentration and periods of rest.

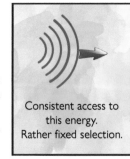

Consistent access to this energy.
Rather fixed selection.

Learn how to work with the energy of this center otherwise you might burn out your adrenals ('burn out' symptom).

In our culture our energy (Pulse Center) is expected to be 'on' (i.e. able to focus) all the time. If this is not the case then some medication is often prescribed. (Think about children at school that can't focus).

**Powerful motor
when the pulse is on.**

Look at your **Human Design Chart** and color the Root Center below if it is defined (colored) on your chart.

53 60 52
54   19
38   39
58   41

OPEN: 50% of the POPULATION

May feel like the work is never done.
Beware of trying to get too much done.
Have an ongoing To-Do list and struggle to get it all done.
Ask what the worst is that will happen if things don't get done?

The trick is to not always obey the open root energy! Be aware of this pressure center.
There can be different levels of sensitivity in this center.
It is easy to feel under pressure if someone with an open root is with someone with a defined root. It is not personal.

Best to follow your Strategy per Type

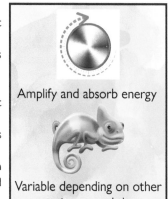

Amplify and absorb energy

Variable depending on other energies around them

The 4 'Motors' (Centers)

‹uh-huh / uh-uh›
Yes / No questions

The Motors can be considered
as a booster or additional energy
supply to the Centers.

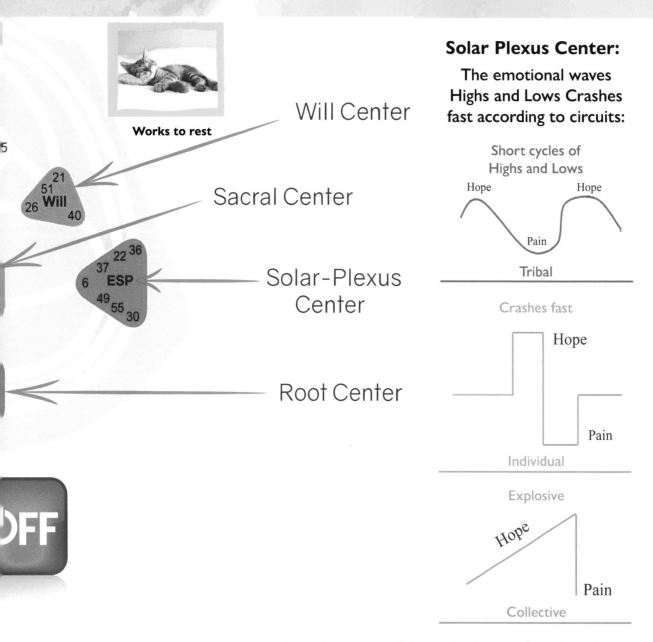

Works to rest

Will Center

Sacral Center

Solar-Plexus Center

Root Center

21
51
26 **Will**
40

22 36
37
6 **ESP**
49 55 30

OFF

Solar Plexus Center:

The emotional waves Highs and Lows Crashes fast according to circuits:

Short cycles of Highs and Lows

Hope   Hope

Pain

Tribal

Crashes fast

Hope

Pain

Individual

Explosive

Hope

Pain

Collective

Look at your **Human Design chart** and write down the information on the following pages:

Do I have defined motor centers?

_____

How many motor centers are defined?

_____

_____

Which motor Centers are defined?

_____

Section Four

Profiles

Look at your **HUMAN DESIGN CHART** and write down your profile (should be shown on your Chart). It is derived from the number next to the Gate number of the **SUN** ☉ and the **EARTH** ⊕ symbols.

The **CONSCIOUS** number (in **black** under **Personality**) is written first and then the UNCONSCIOUS number (in red under Design) next to it.

1) My **PROFILE** is:

_____

2) My **CONSCIOUS** line (black number) is:

    1   2   3   4   5   6

3) This line has the following role associated with it:

_____

4) My **UNCONSCIOUS** line (red number) is:

    1   2   3   4   5   6

5) This line has the following role associated with it:

_____

EXPLANATION of the 12 PROFILES

In Human Design, there are 12 Profiles.

The Profile number comes from:

- the lines of the Personality (Mind) and the Design (Body)
- the Sun and Earth Gates and
- is usually shown on the Human Design Chart.

Profile Example

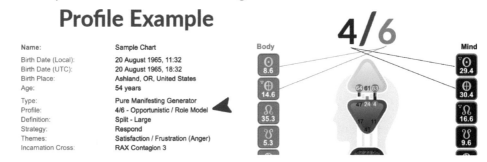

Name:	Sample Chart
Birth Date (Local):	20 August 1965, 11:32
Birth Date (UTC):	20 August 1965, 18:32
Birth Place:	Ashland, OR, United States
Age:	54 years
Type:	Pure Manifesting Generator
Profile:	4/6 - Opportunistic / Role Model
Definition:	Split - Large
Strategy:	Respond
Themes:	Satisfaction / Frustration (Anger)
Incarnation Cross:	RAX Contagion 3

The 12 Profiles

Personal Profiles 1/3 through 3/6   *Transpersonal Profiles (i.e., 4/6 to 6/3)*

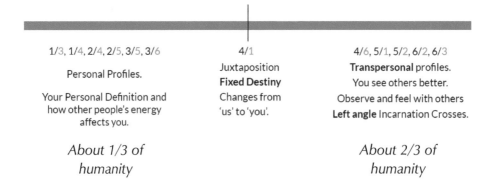

1/3, 1/4, 2/4, 2/5, 3/5, 3/6	4/1	4/6, 5/1, 5/2, 6/2, 6/3
Personal Profiles.	Juxtaposition **Fixed Destiny**	**Transpersonal** profiles. You see others better.
Your Personal Definition and how other people's energy affects you.	Changes from 'us' to 'you'.	Observe and feel with others **Left angle** Incarnation Crosses.
About 1/3 of humanity		*About 2/3 of humanity*

The two Profile numbers show how these energy combinations influence your learning style and how someone goes through life.

However, it is important to look at the whole Chart to get the bigger picture.
The individual pieces of the Chart contribute to a better understanding of the Chart as a whole.

The lines are taken from the I'Ching hexagrams.

The Resource	Line 6 Role Model
The Responder	Line 5 Heretic
The Explorer	Line 4 Opportunist
The Foundation	Line 3 Martyr / Experimenter
The Visionary Leader	Line 2 Hermit
The Adept	Line 1 Investigator

The planets move around the Mandala through

each Gate and each line at varying speeds.

The Sun takes 365 days.

Each Gate has 6 lines.

Movement is counterclockwise.

LINE 1: THE INVESTIGATOR

Line 1 is foundational.
1st lines like to go in-depth and investigate everything.

Naturally curious.

Need a good foundation of information to feel secure and safe in this world.

Need to investigate and learn everything.

LOW EXPRESSION:	**HIGH EXPRESSION:**
Fear of the unknown. Might miss out on an experience.	Deeply knowledgeable.

1/3 Investigative Martyr (Experimenter)

About 15% of humanity

1/4 Investigative Opportunist

About 2% of humanity

Line 1: Needs a solid basis

Line 3: As soon as something is incorrect, everything is overturned and starts anew (sometimes considered an anarchist).

Line 4: Waits for the right opportunity and brings their knowledge to others (networkers/ friends/ groups).

LINE 2: THE HERMIT

2nd Line profiles like and need alone time.

Generally, they get called out and seen by others the more they hide away.

Shyness and loneliness in life. Love alone time, also to regenerate.

The more they hide, the more likely they are to be seen and called out by others.

LOW EXPRESSION:

Hide out and miss the joys of life.

HIGH EXPRESSION:

Wait to be called out to the right experiences. Take time to regenerate and renew.

2/4 Hermit Opportunist

About 15% of humanity

2/5 Hermit Heretic

About 2% of humanity

Line 2: Likes doing their own thing

Line 4: Training and encouragement. Get called out and come together with the right people.

Line 5: Important to keep at a distance. People project their expectations on those with the line 5.

LINE 3: MARTYR / EXPERIMENTER

3rd lines like to experiment to find out what works and what does not so that others can benefit from their experience.

There is not a right or wrong and, therefore, no mistakes. From their experiments, others learn what is useful.

Are supposed to try out many things - it is clear that not everything is supposed to be successful. That is their purpose - to find out what works; it's not about not making any 'mistakes'! 'Mistakes' are part of the learning curve and are to be valued and appreciated! You should not be punished for making 'mistakes'. Others benefit from your results.

LOW EXPRESSION:	HIGH EXPRESSION:
Fear of trying out new things because a certain amount of experimentation ('trial and error') is involved.	Wise about life, based on your own experiences.
3/5 Martyr Heretic	**3/6** Martyr Role Model
About 15% of humanity	About 2% of humanity

Line 3: Experimenter - Trial and Error

Line 5: Questions everything and finds solutions. So-called 'mistakes' help us to advance.

Line 6: Has three Phases. Through life experience, set an example and show us what works.

LINE 4: OPPORTUNIST

(sometimes called an influencer)
4th lines do not like living in limbo (uncertainty).
Must be able to move directly from one thing to the next.

It is a transpersonal line. Gate themes are lived out more in relationships. Wants to get to the foundation of what it means to live in relationships. Cares deeply, and a deep foundation of friendship is needed to feel secure even in romantic relationships. Is waiting for the right opportunity to share.

Doesn't make changes very easily and likes things to stay the same.

LOW EXPRESSION:	HIGH EXPRESSION:
Afraid to speak your truth and fix things, you just create an alternative and move on, sometimes not dealing with the challenges.	Consistent, stable, and a good friend.

4/1 Opportunist Investigator

About 2% of humanity

4/6 Opportunist Role Model

About 15% of humanity

Line 4: Opportunities and Networking
It is a connection point between personal destiny and trans-personal Karma.
Rather rare profile line. Can be very flexible or very stubborn.

Line 1: The foundation has to be right. In-depth training is important to be able to give out the information.

Line 6: Goes through three phases on an unconscious level. Role model in cooperation with others.

LINE 5: HERETIC

5th lines have a compelling, charismatic, seductive, persuasive power.
They 'have to' go out and be in relationships and be connected.

 Expectations are projected onto them. People can have correct or wrong expectations. People see what they need themselves - and not the real you - you are a karmic (energetic) mirror for others, showing them what they need to heal and align their energy.

LOW EXPRESSION:	HIGH EXPRESSION:
Use charm or personal gain and sometimes hurt others.	Successfully influence people.

5/1 Investigative **Heretic**

About 15% of humanity
Bring practical solutions to difficult situations.
Requirement to withdraw themselves.
Attractive, compelling energy for others.

5/2 Heretic Hermit

About 2% of humanity
High expectations. Like to withdraw.

Line 5: 'Karmic Mirror'
(Other's expectations are projected on to them)

Line 1: The foundation has to be correct; otherwise, the expectations cannot be fulfilled.

Line 2: Distance is important.
 –Seem more compelling (attracting).
Like to be left alone.

LINE 6: ROLE MODEL

6th lines have a somewhat fixed destiny with not much leeway.
Are supposed to BE a role model for others.
Are the observers.

Is lived out in 3 phases:

1. **Birth to 28.6 years - Experiment**
All about experiences and experimentation (like 3rd line).

2. **Age 28.6 years to about 50 years**
Life doesn't feel so lively as it was during the twenties. Might feel like things use up a lot of energy. Often referred to as 'being on the roof' (may seem like emotional indifference – observing from a distance).

3. **Around 50 years onwards** come 'off the roof' and move toward creating a life that is a full manifestation of your authentic self. This is the role model phase.

LOW EXPRESSION:	HIGH EXPRESSION:
Get stuck in aloofness and struggle to get back into the world.	BE a role model who inspires others.
6/2 Role model Hermit	**6/3** Role Model Martyr
About 15% of humanity	About 2% of humanity

Line 6: BE a role model example for others

Line 2: Withdrawal and alone time are important.

Line 3: Lots of experimentation.
Not all of the experiments are supposed to be successful. It's about finding what works– there are no mistakes. 1st phase = double experimenter!

OVERVIEW OF THE 6 PROFILES:

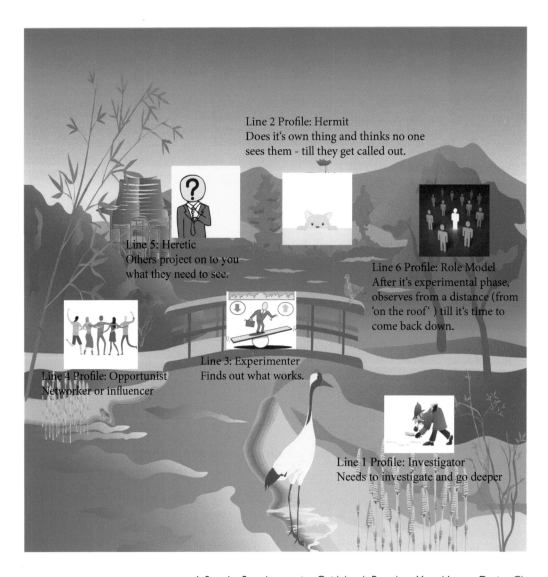

Line 2 Profile: Hermit
Does it's own thing and thinks no one
sees them - till they get called out.

Line 5: Heretic
Others project on to you
what they need to see.

Line 6 Profile: Role Model
After it's experimental phase,
observes from a distance (from
'on the roof') till it's time to
come back down.

Line 4 Profile: Opportunist
Networker or influencer

Line 3: Experimenter
Finds out what works.

Line 1 Profile: Investigator
Needs to investigate and go deeper

Section Five
Authority

AUTHORITY

As the head is not designed to make decisions (but to make comparisons and analyze) our inner authority (Center) helps us with decision making. Authority flavors the way you use your strategy.

This is the Center that is defined and connected to the Throat Center - this influences the decision making process. Ra, the founder of Human Design, originally mentioned only three main authority Centers (Sacral Center, Spleen Center and Emotional Solar Plexus Center).

Your authority is usually stated on your Human Design Chart .

When more than one Center is defined in your chart, then the centers are prioritized as follows:

1. Solar Plexus Center defined = Emotional Authority (wait out the emotional wave).
Around 47%

2. Sacral Center defined = Sacral Authority (only Generator Types). Pay attention to your Sacral Around 35% response (gut feeling) in the moment.
Only Generators and Manifesting Generators.

3. Spleen Center defined = Splenic authority (intuitive impulse in the moment).
Around 11%
Only Manifestors and Projectors

THE FOLLOWING TERMS ARE ALSO USED IN HUMAN DESIGN:

4. Will Center defined = Ego Authority (Heart Manifested), Will Center to Throat
Around 1%
Only Manifestors and Projectors

5. G-Center defined = Self-projected Authority, G-Center (Heart) to the Throat
Around 3%
Only Projectors

6. Ajna Center defined = Mental Projected Authority, Ajna to Throat and/or Head Center.
Around 3% Also called Environmental.
Only Projectors.

Also look at the descriptions of each of the Centers under 'The Centers' section in this book.

Outer Authority is when the mind is liberated from decision making tasks for which it was never designed. Then what we say can be inspiring for others. The mind second-guesses our true authority and can argue for or against whatever serves it best.

DEFINED CENTERS THAT GIVE INNER AUTHORITY

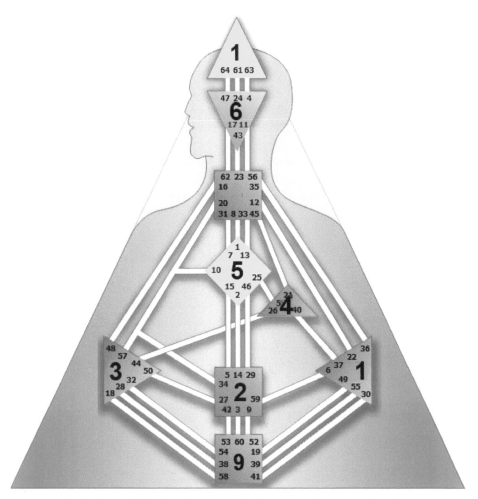

Order in which the Centers define your inner authority

Section Six

Gates

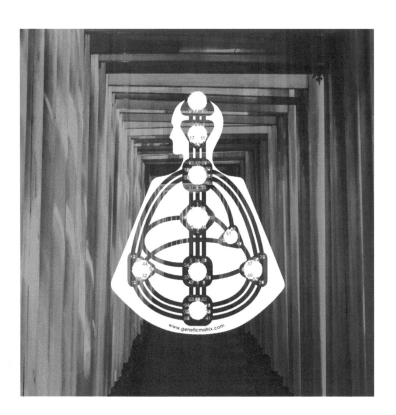

GATES in HUMAN DESIGN

THERE ARE 64 GATES THAT CORRESPOND TO THE 64 HEXAGRAMS OF THE I'CHING.

These are a representation of the human archetypes.

Two Defined Gates that are connected are called a Channel.
Definition can be **red** and **black** checked, or only **red** or only **black**.
A Channel defines the Center at each end.

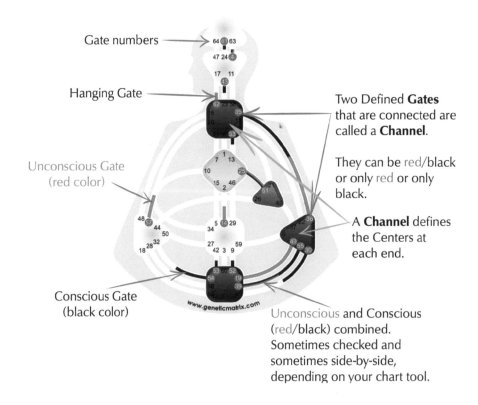

Gate numbers

Hanging Gate

Unconscious Gate
(red color)

Conscious Gate
(black color)

www.geneticmatrix.com

Two Defined **Gates**
that are connected are
called a **Channel**.

They can be red/black
or only red or only
black.

A **Channel** defines
the Centers at
each end.

Unconscious and Conscious
(red/black) combined.
Sometimes checked and
sometimes side-by-side,
depending on your chart tool.

MY UNCONSCIOUS GATES

Physical Body
(Vehicle)

Unconscious Gates are always red in color on the chart.

DESIGN/LIFE PURPOSE

Design/Unconscious Gates are from the planetary positions at 88 degrees (astrologically) before effective time of birth (i.e. approximately three months before birth).

These are the themes of your **Life Purpose.**

Look at your Human Design Chart and find the Gates that are colored red and red/**black.** Color the corresponding Gates on the Circuit Chart below, preferably using a red color.

MY CONSCIOUS GATES

Conscious Gates are always black in color on the chart.

PERSONALITY/SOUL PURPOSE

Personality/conscious Gates are from the planetary positions at time of birth. These are the themes of your **Soul Purpose.**

Mind
(Passenger)

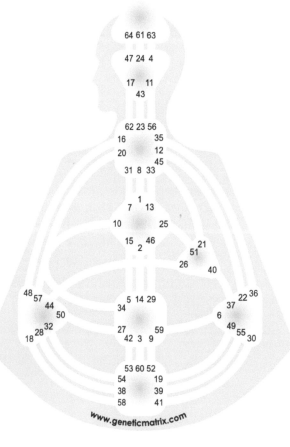

Look at your Human Design Chart and find the Gates that are colored **black** and **red**/**black.** Color the corresponding Gates on the Circuit Chart below, preferably using a **black** color.

www.geneticmatrix.com

KEYNOTES INTRODUCTION

HERE IS A VERY BRIEF OVERVIEW OF THE 64 GATES SO YOU CAN GET AN IDEA OF THE THEMES OF the gates and how they impact you. Keynotes are the essence of the meanings for each Gate.

The gates are based on the 64 Chinese I'Ching hexagrams. Please also be aware of the fact that each Gate is in one of 6 lines at any given time - which also gives the gate expression a slightly different nuance on its main theme.

If you look at the Human Design Mandala, you see the gates are in a particular position that relate to the astrological signs.

The Sun moves through the gates and each of the 6 lines in a counter-clockwise direction starting at Gate 41 (usually around 22nd January of each year).

This reference is organized numerically by Gate and indicates:

The characteristics of the Gate including:

- Gate name,
- Center location,
- Channel designation

Each gate's location in circuitry based on this color code:

- Blue = Individual Circuit, including the Integration Circuit
- **Brown = Tribal Circuit**
- Green = collective Circuit

We'll explore Circuits in the next section.

Please note that there is a wide spectrum of how these energies get expressed ranging from not being expressed at all to being fully expressed (in an optimal or repressed way). This list only shows the original energy blueprint activated at birth and not how it is being expressed.

Using your Human Design chart,find those Gates that are defined for you and mark either the **red** or **black** check box, as indicated in your chart, next to each Gate on the following pages.

KEYNOTES - GATES 1-5

☐ ☐ **Gate 1 QHD Purpose**
Self expression / Beauty
G-Center
Channel 1-8

Contribution from the Soul.
Strongest Yang-Yang Gate.
Individuality and Self-Empowerment.

☐ ☐ **Gate 2 QHD Allowing**
Keeper of Keys / Trust
Seat of Magnetic Monopole
G-Center
Channel 2-14

Manage wealth and resources.
Strongest Yin-Yin Gate.

☐ ☐ **Gate 3 QHD Innovation**
Ordering/Synthesis
Sacral Center
Channel 3-60

Mutative

☐ ☐ **Gate 4 QHD Possibility**
Answers/Understanding
Ajna Center
Channel 4-63

Possibilities - not Truth
Is Head energy. Does not know if
the answer is correct.

☐ ☐ **Gate 5 QHD Consistency**
Fixed Patterns/Patience
Sacral Center
Channel 5-15

Needs routines / Rhythm.
Relatively fixed. In tune with natural
order and rhythms of nature.

KEYNOTES - GATES 6-10

☐ ☐ **Gate 6 Impact**
Friction/Diplomatic
Solar Plexus Center
Channel 6-59

Aura busting, Yang-side of defense. Resources and reproduction (Sex or war).

☐ ☐ **Gate 7 Collaborator**
Self in Interaction/Chief of Staff
G-Center
Channel 7-31

Supported Leadership.
Leads best with someone who has Gate 31

☐ ☐ **Gate 8 Fullfillment**
Contribution/Exquisiteness
Throat Center
Channel 1-8

Creative Role model. Gives direction.

☐ ☐ **Gate 9 Narrowimg**
Focus/Determination
Sacral Center
Channel 9-52

Focused for short periods of time.
Potential for compulsive behavior.

☐ ☐ **Gate 10 Self-Love**
Love of Self/Empowerment
G-Center
Channels 10-57 / 10-20 / 10-34

Empowers others. Often blamed. Voice comes from the Soul (G-Center). Pay attention to words especially with Gate 20.

KEYNOTES - GATES 11-15

☐ ☐ **Gate 11 The Conceptualist**
Ideas/Inspiration
Ajna Center
Channel 11-56

Seeker. Ideas are to be shared with others - not for yourself. Very creative.

☐ ☐ **Gate 12 The Channel**
Caution/Higher principles
Throat Center
Channel 12-22

Connection to super consciousness. Tone of voice plays a big role. Attuned to something bigger.

☐ ☐ **Gate 13 Narrative**
Listener /Show compassion
G-Center
Channel 13-33

People share their secrets. Good historians. Bring the energy of the past into the present. Forgiveness and share.

☐ ☐ **Gate 14 Creation**
Power skills /bountiful
Sacral Center
Channel 14-2

Resources come easily. Lucky.

☐ ☐ **Gate 15 Compassion**
Extremes/Magnetism
Love of humanity
G-Center
Channel 15-5

Big Aura. No routine. Extreme.

KEYNOTES - GATES 16-20

☐ ☐ **Gate 16 Zest**
Skills/Mastery/Enthusiam
Throat Center
Channel 16-48

Can just do it. Skills, but no depth.
Wait! Don't just do it! Have to gain
mastery to nurture that talent.

☐ ☐ **Gate 17 Anticipation**
Opinions/Mature awareness of
possibilities
Ajna Center
Channel 17-62

Hypothesis, new ideas, opinions.
Beware that opinions are not
mistaken for facts.

☐ ☐ **Gate 18 Re-alignment**
Correction/Integrity/ Perfectionist
Spleen Center
Channel 18-58

Find the perfect patterns.
Healer: Recognizes and corrects
patterns. Fear of not being perfect.

☐ ☐ **Gate 19 Attunement**
Wanting/Super sensitive
Root Center
Channel 19-49

Very sensitive to touch and feelings
and what others need.
19-49 channel for Love and
marriage. Important that everything
feels right.

☐ ☐ **Gate 20 Patience**
Metamorphosis
Throat Center
Channel 20-10/57/34

Individual voice. Collective
Leadership. Assess talents and skills
of others.
Potential: Critic or publisher.

KEYNOTES - GATES 21-25

☐ ☐ **Gate 21 Self-Regulation**
Treasurer/Executive/Authority
Will Center
Channel 21-45

Control physical resources. Budget.
Conflict potential between partners
who have Gates 21 and 45.

☐ ☐ **Gate 22 Surrender**
Openness/Graciousness
Grace
Solar Plexus Center

Can 'work the room'.
Can have auditory or speech
themes. Must master inner beauty
and grace.

☐ ☐ **Gate 23 Transmission**
Assimilation/Simplicity/
Quintessence
Throat Center
Channel 23-43

Freak or Genius? Transformer. Finds
the useful pieces to share. Internal
head dialogue (touch softly to gain
their attention).

☐ ☐ **Gate 24 Blessings**
Rationalize/Invention/Silence
Ajna Center
Channel 24-61

What can be used?
Deep understanding. Can rationalize
anything - find what works.

☐ ☐ **Gate 25 Spirit**
Love of Spirit/Certainty
G-Center
Channel 25-51

Natural healing abilities –
Power of Love. Allow self
to BE part of the divine and trust the
divine order of things.

☐ ☐ **Gate 26 Integrity**
Trickster/Integrity
Will Center
Channel 26-44

Close the deal or the sale.
Seller. Passes the idea on to be taken
up by others. Good teacher.
Integrity - truth or not!

☐ ☐ **Gate 27 Accountability**
Responsibility /Altruism
Sacral Center
Channel 27-50

Mother Teresa Energy - for the
collective. Give up the individual for
the good of the whole. Conformity
to the Tribe mandatory. Values,
education important to share.

☐ ☐ **Gate 28 Adventure/Challenge**
Struggle/ fight way through/
Evolution
Spleen Center
Channel 28-38

Life might seem hard.
Learn the hard way. Others learn
from their experiences. What's
worth fighting for. Shock Effect.

☐ ☐ **Gate 29 Devotion**
Perseverence/Devotion
G-Center
Channel 29-46

Commitment
Can be successful where others fail.
Learn to say No.

☐ ☐ **Gate 30 Passion**
Desire /Passion, 10x Intensity
Solarplexus-Zentrum
Channel 41-30

Create new experiences.
Burn Out danger. Amplifies
everything on the Chart 10-fold.
Holds up the desire till the timing is
right.

KEYNOTES - GATES 31-35

☐ ☐ **Gate 31 The Leader**
Democracy/Humble leadership
Throat Center
Channel 31-7

Be of service. Must be recognized (otherwise are angry dictators). Bring power together, delegate, and share.

☐ ☐ **Gate 32 Endurance**
Continuity/Conservation
Spleen Center
Channel 32-54

Sees the ideas and knows which ones to follow. Fears (Spleen Center) Only functions when comes from place of love and is for the good of the whole.

☐ ☐ **Gate 33 Re-telling**
Privacy/Storyteller
Throat Center
Channel 33-13

What needs to be shared. Historian. Maintains memory of the collective. Shares stories when the timing is right

☐ ☐ **Gate 34 Power**
Power /Majesty/Strength
Sacral Center
Channel 34-57/20/10

Must always be busy. Designed to do many things at once (not stick to one thing!) Energy must be correctly expressed.

☐ ☐ **Gate 35 Experience**
Change/Adventure/
Boundlessness
Throat Center
Channel 35-36

What experiences are worth it? Jack of all trades. Challenge to follow something passionately. Boredom is a big theme. Must be worth their while, otherwise can't be bothered.

KEYNOTES - GATES 36-40

☐ ☐ **Gate 36 Exploration**
Crisis/Explore/Adventure
Solar Plexus-Center
Channel 36-35

Impulsive, easily bored. Don't wait.
Change: Studies/Job.
Boredom is scary - want the next
new experience. Emotional. Push to
the limit!

☐ ☐ **Gate 37 Harmony**
Inner Peace/Harmony
Solar Plexus Center
Channel 37-40

Harmony and Peace. Contracts and
agreements. Want clarity.

☐ ☐ **Gate 38 Visionary**
Fighter
Root Center
Channel 38-28

Stubborn, what is worth fighting for.
Feeling of not belonging. Addictions.
Pushes to find life purpose.

☐ ☐ **Gate 39 Re-calibration**
Provocation/ Liberation/ Activist
Will Center
Channel 39-55

Pokes. bargain hunter, hoarder.
Emotional ways of coping
(eg. food-diabetes, weight projects).
Provokes. Tension created in body.

☐ ☐ **Gate 40 Restoration**
Aloneness Resolve
Will Center
Channel 40-37

Loner seeking their Tribe. Feels alone
in a crowd of people. How they feel
does not necessarily reflect their
reality. Likes healthy alone time and
boundaries.

KEYNOTES - GATES 41-45

☐ ☐ **Gate 41 Imagination**
Fantasy/Inventive Imagination
Root Center
Channel 41-30

Bring new ideas and experiences
into form. Daydreamer (right
brained). Very creative. *Beginning of
Human Design New Year.*

☐ ☐ **Gate 42 Conclusion**
Finish things /Celebrate
Sacral Center
Channel 42-53

Finish projects.
Good consultants - realign and fix
things.
Need help starting things.

☐ ☐ **Gate 43 Insight**
Insight / Empathy
Ajna Center
Channel 43-23

See new alternatives.
Challenging to express the insight.
Instantaneous insights.

☐ ☐ **Gate 44 Truth**
Presentation/Teamwork/Salesperson
Spleen Center
Channel 44-26

Make things look good: branding and
packaging. Sets up the sale. Excellent
sense of smell. Bring lessons of the
past into the present to be healed.
Fear of the past and of repeating past
mistakes.

☐ ☐ **Gate 45 Dispensation**
King or Queen/Natural regal
leadership
Throat Center
Channel 45-21

Influences the Tribe.
Knows the resources and distributes
them.

KEYNOTES - GATES 46-50

☐ ☐ **Gate 46 Embodiment**
Love of the Flesh/ Vitality
G-Center
Channel 46-29

Moving life force through the physical body. The body is the vehicle for the Soul. Any misalignment shows up as physical distortion of the body. Often seen doing yoga, teaching, dancing, photographing.

☐ ☐ **Gate 47 Mindset**
Realization / Positive Expectation
Ajna Center
Channel 47-64

Trust and Faith (mindset and attitude).

☐ ☐ **Gate 48 Wisdom**
Depth /Wisdom
Spleen Center
Channel 48-16

Fear of inadequacy, not knowing enough. (Fear of the Spleen Center). Should just push through and do it anyway. Has to go deep down the rabbit hole. Good sense of taste - may be picky eaters.

☐ ☐ **Gate 49 Revolution**
Principles/Wise
Solar Plexus Center
Channel 49-19

Rules are rules – must be followed. Divorce Gate. No compromises if rules are broken. Emotional Energy

☐ ☐ **Gate 50 Nurturing**
Values/Harmony
Spleen Center
Channel 50-27

Must obey the rules and values of the Tribe (overrides the individual circuit). Greatest fear is not being able to take care of loved ones. Cooking = Love. High sense of responsibility. Instinct to take care of others (Yin energy).

KEYNOTES - GATES 51-55

☐ ☐ **Gate 51 Initiation**
Shock/Initiation
Will Center
Channel 51-25

Intensive life changing experiences. Being polite is not a theme here!! Is a catalyst for deep growth and evolution. Shock for change - to lead us back to love of Spirit.

☐ ☐ **Gate 52 Perspective**
Stillness/ Reserved
Root Center
Channel 52-9

Concentration for long periods. Guidance comes from the stillness. Waits for interesting opportunity (pulse energy from Root center). Creative energy. Good wildlife photographer.

☐ ☐ **Gate 53 Starting**
Starting Things/Expansion
Root Center
Channel 53-42

Energy to start things, but not finish them.
Allow self (and children) to NOT finish things is about the experience) not the result.

☐ ☐ **Gate 54 Divine Inspiration**
Drive/ Aspiration Ambition
Root Center
Channel 54-32

Know how to wait and trust that the correct direction will be shown. Can be busy and work until they collapse. Is the Chief-Dreamer. Can only manifest when recognized.

☐ ☐ **Gate 55 Faith**
Spirit /Freedom /Abundance
Solar Plexus Center
Channel 55-39

Trust in the natural abundance of Spirit. Learn the abundance of Spirit/Source on a soul level. Restore self and others back to the divine order flow of abundance. Deeply mystical Gate.

KEYNOTES - GATES 56-60

☐ ☐ **Gate 56 Expansion**
Storyteller /Enriching
Throat Center
Channel 56-11

Uses metaphors and stories to share and teach. Can be good teachers.

☐ ☐ **Gate 57 Instinct**
Intuition /High awareness now
Spleen Center
Channel 57-20/10

Intuition and awareness in the NOW. Most intuitive Gate in Human Design. Gate of clarity. What is correct now may change in the next moment. Difficult to trust intuition and oneself. Fear of the future (Spleen Center).

☐ ☐ **Gate 58 The Joy of Mastery**
Joy of Life /Blissfull devotion
Root Center
Channel 58-18

Don't take things too seriously. Align back with own joy to get others in their joy. Is possible to lose joy of life when not living in alignment with your path and not living your strategy.

☐ ☐ **Gate 59 Sustainability**
Sexuality /intimacy
Sacral Center
Channel 59-6

Seductive/compelling, needs time to bond. Right side (Defense Circuit): work, aggressive.
Defend sexuality (Yang quality).

☐ ☐ **Gate 60 Conservation**
Acceptance/Inventive/Resources
Root Center
Channel 60-3

Wants to evolve. Brings mutation. Accepts the limitations of change and makes the best of it. Old genetic information meets up with new genetic information to create mutation.

KEYNOTES - GATES 61-64

☐ ☐ **Gate 61 Wonder**
Mystery/ Wonder
Head Center
Channel 61-24

WHY? Big thinker - big questions seeking answers. Claircognizant- Just knows, but doesn't know how they know. Least practical Gate in Chart. Lost in thoughts.

☐ ☐ **Gate 62 Preparation**
Details/Precision
Throat Center
Channel 62-17

Detailed, organized, and methodical. Can get stuck in patterns and details and not see the big picture. Designed to see if energy from Gate 17 is correct. Logical.

☐ ☐ **Gate 63 Curiosity**
Doubt/Inquiring
Head Center
Channel 63-4

WHAT? Can you prove it? Doubt pointed at outer world, not yourself! Often don't trust own intuition. Curious. Right eye /left brain.

☐ ☐ **Gate 64 Divine Transference**
Confusion/Enlightenment
Head Center
Channel 64-47

HOW? Inspiring downloads. Visual. Left eye / right brain. Confusion - sees the whole picture, but does not know how to bring the ideas into form.

Section Seven

Circuits

CIRCUITS

IN HUMAN DESIGN, EACH CHANNEL HAS A RELATIONSHIP TO A SERIES OF OTHER CHANNELS. These groupings are called circuits and also have sub-circuits. Circuits are like the electrical wiring in a house. Each person has their own unique wiring.

All the Channels within a circuit create and share a larger theme so they can't be separated. What makes it to the Throat Center is the most influential.

Circuits show if you have Individual, Tribal, or Collective energies. Most people have a mixture of all the circuits. There is nobody that exists with only one circuit. For some people, one particular theme can be more predominant. There may also be some challenges in the combination of themes of the circuit that want to be expressed.

There is a natural affinity between people with the same Circuits.

There are three main Circuits, each with two sub-Circuits.

- Individual, (Knowing and Centering)
- Tribal, (Defense and Ego)
- Collective (Understanding and Sensing)

The Integration Circuit is an independent Circuit, but has some Gates that also belong to the Individual Circuit.

Even if you have only one Gate defined in any Circuit, you have part of that Circuit's energy.

OVERVIEW of the CIRCUITS

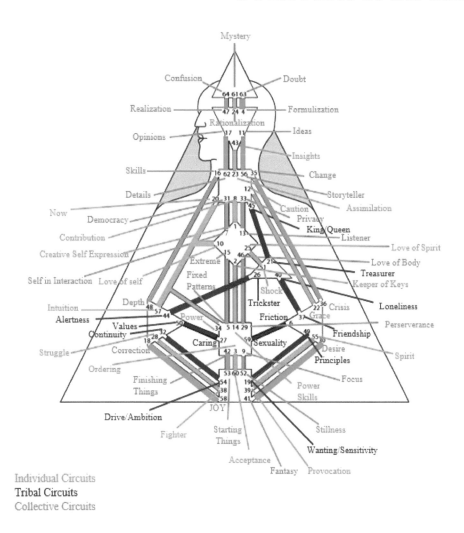

Individual Circuits
Tribal Circuits
Collective Circuits

INDIVIDUAL **CIRCUIT**

Brings change – is mutative. Tries out and shows what works.
Brings new paradigms and ideas.
Can feel different as though they don't belong or fit in anywhere.

Two Sub-Circuits Centering and Knowing.
These have the theme of Self-Empowerment.

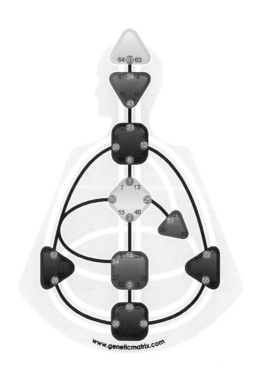

www.geneticmatrix.com

CENTERING CIRCUIT

'Aura busting' energy
Has 2 Motors

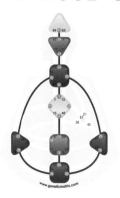

KNOWING CIRCUIT

You know that you know, but not
how you know
Has 3 Motors

INTEGRATION CIRCUIT

Is a Circuit in itself with some Individual Gates
Has 1 Motor

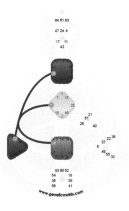

TRIBAL **CIRCUIT**

Adapts
Aura-busting - very powerful compelling energy.
You have to comply and maintain the rules and values of the tribe.
Demands sacrifice of the individual.

Two Sub-Circuits: Defense and Ego
Takes care of the family / Tribe

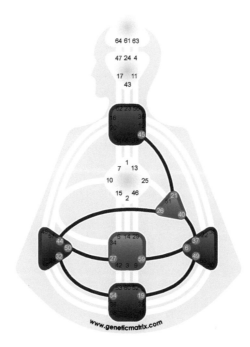

www.geneticmatrix.com

DEFENSE CIRCUIT

Left side (27-50): Nurturing energy. Cares for the family, food, education, etc. Survival in the NOW. (Spleen Center)

Right side (59-6): Energy for work, resources and reproduction.

Has 2 Motors

EGO CIRCUIT

Left side: Business: contracts, resources, sales.

Right side: Social: intimacy, principles, rules and laws.

Has 3 Motors

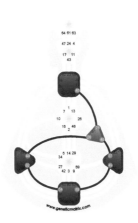

COLLECTIVE **CIRCUIT**

Adopts.
Looks out for the well-being of the whole; sharing.
100th monkey syndrome.

Two sub-circuits: Understanding (Logic) and Sensing Abstract

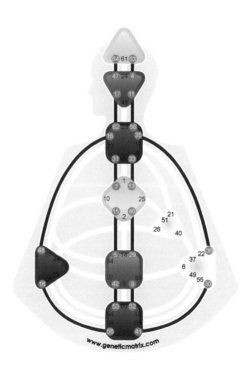

UNDERSTANDING
CIRCUIT (Logic)

About repetition and consistent exposure.

Understanding is obtained over time.

Left Brain.

Has 2 Motors

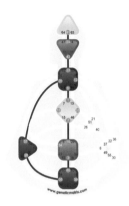

SENSING
CIRCUIT (Abstract)

About assimilating the past- emotional, expansive.

Linear stories, storytelling experiences, and emotional

energy (Emotional Solar Plexus).

Visual right brain.

Has 3 Motors.

INTEGRATION **CIRCUIT**

Life Purpose Design
Body (Vehicle)

57-20 Brainwave
Awareness is the NOW.
Brings the right people and talents
intuitively together.
Part of the Knowing Circuit.

10-20 Awakening
(Buddha Channel)
Commit to higher principles.
Beware - can be a verbal gunslinger
(words can hurt).

57-10 Perfected Form
Survival. Intuition tells you if you
are in alignment with your Self.
Want to empower others.

34-10 Exploration
Power through BE-ing and responding.
Part of the Centering Circuit.

34-57 Power
Intuitive Lifeforce Energy.
Highly Auditory.

34-20 Charisma
Busy doing things.
Powerful Sacral energy
to the Throat.

With a **red** marker, color your defined **Design (unconscious) Gates** and **red/black** checked Gates as shown on your Human Design Chart

Channels:
34-57
34-10 Also part of the Centering Circuit
34-20
57-10
57-20 Also part of the Knowing Circuit
10-20

General Characteristics of the Integration Circuit:

People with any of these Channels have to be self-sufficient (have own car, account, pay for their own dinner).

It's not about sharing. Without Gates 28 (Spleen), 38 (Root), or 34 (Sacral) the Theme is **SELF-Empowerment.**

Some Gates may also be in the other Sub-Circuits of the Individual Circuits on the following pages.

Self Empowerment

Now, locate your Gates and Channels for each Circuit. The chart examples starting on the following pages are organized with descriptive text on the left and images on the right. They are used together to give you a complete understanding of the channels for that circuit. Find and color your Design Gates on the left page and your **Personality** Gates on the right.

Soul Purpose
Personality (Passenger)

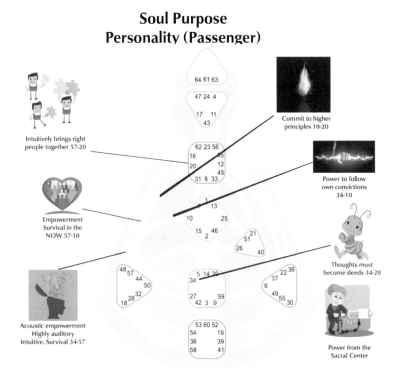

With a **black** marker, color your defined **Personality (conscious) Gates** and red/**black** checked Gates as shown on your Human Design Chart

Intuitively brings right people together 57-20

Empowerment Survival in the NOW 57-10

Acoustic empowerment Highly auditory Intuitive. Survival 34-57

Commit to higher principles 10-20

Power to follow own convictions 34-10

Thoughts must become deeds 34-20

Power from the Sacral Center

Channels:
34-57
34-10 Also part of the Centering Circuit
34-20
57-10
57-20 Also part of the Knowing Circuit
10-20

Some Gates may also be in the other Sub-Circuits of the Individual Circuits on the following pages.

INDIVIDUAL CIRCUIT - CENTERING

Life Purpose Design
Body (Vehicle)

With a **red** marker, color your defined **Design** (**unconscious**) **Gates** and **red**/**black** checked Gates as shown on your Human Design Chart

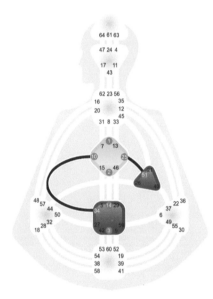

Channels:

25-51

34-10 Also part of the Integration Circuit

General Characteristics of the
Centering Circuit:

Initiates others in the love of Self and Spirit. Can move people energetically into love by BEing.

People drawn into this circuit are influenced to act more individually regardless of own definition.

Initiation through shock can be empowering or alienating depending how you look at it.

Powerful aura busting energy vortex. Very compelling.

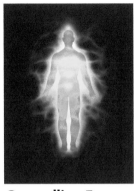

Compelling Energy

Soul Purpose Design
Personality (Passenger)

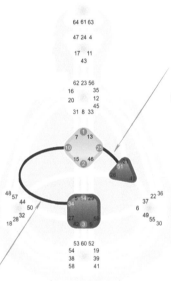

Initiation through
shock (back to spirit)
25-51

With a **black** marker, color your defined **Personality (conscious) Gates** and red/**black** checked Gates as shown on your Human Design Chart

Always busy!
Thoughts to deeds
34-10

Channels:
25-51
34-10 Also part of the
Integration Circuit

INDIVIDUAL CIRCUIT - KNOWING

Life Purpose Design
Body (Vehicle)

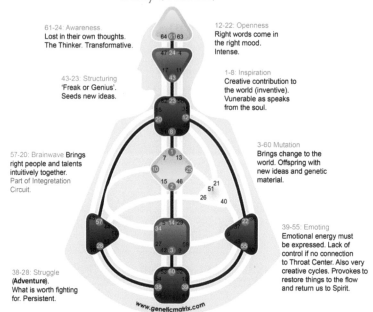

61-24: Awareness.
Lost in their own thoughts.
The Thinker. Transformative.

12-22: Openness
Right words come in
the right mood.
Intense.

43-23: Structuring
'Freak or Genius'.
Seeds new ideas.

1-8: Inspiration
Creative contribution to
the world (inventive).
Vunerable as speaks
from the soul.

57-20: Brainwave Brings
right people and talents
intuitively together.
Part of Integretation
Circuit.

3-60 Mutation
Brings change to the
world. Offspring with
new ideas and genetic
material.

39-55: Emoting
Emotional energy must
be expressed. Lack of
control if no connection
to Throat Center. Also very
creative cycles. Provokes to
restore things to the flow
and return us to Spirit.

38-28: Struggle
(**Adventure**).
What is worth fighting
for. Persistent.

www.geneticmatrix.com

With a **red** marker, color
your defined **Design
(unconscious) Gates** and
red/**black** checked Gates
as shown on your Human
Design Chart

Channels:
61-24
43-23
20-57 Also part of the
Integration Circuit
28-38
39-55
22-12
60-3
14-2
1-8

General Characteristics of the
Knowing Circuit:

Largest circuit of all the Circuits. Is the only Circuit with left and right side of
the Chart and three potential motors.

Knows that it knows, but not how it knows.

Potential for self-doubt.

Mutates tribe and collective when timing is right.

Can get lost in thoughts, insights, and feelings.

Share the message that it is important to celebrate their uniqueness – they are
here to be different!

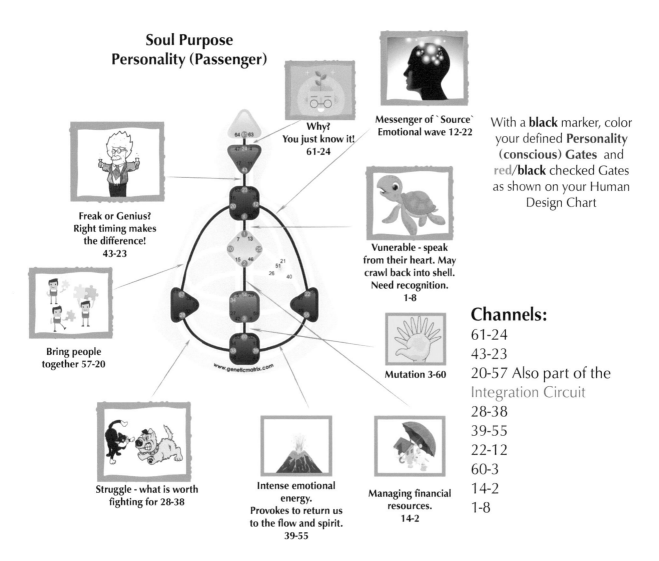

Soul Purpose
Personality (Passenger)

Why?
You just know it!
61-24

Messenger of `Source`
Emotional wave 12-22

With a **black** marker, color your defined **Personality (conscious) Gates** and **red**/**black** checked Gates as shown on your Human Design Chart

Freak or Genius?
Right timing makes the difference!
43-23

Vunerable - speak from their heart. May crawl back into shell. Need recognition.
1-8

Bring people together 57-20

Mutation 3-60

Channels:

61-24
43-23
20-57 Also part of the Integration Circuit
28-38
39-55
22-12
60-3
14-2
1-8

Struggle - what is worth fighting for 28-38

Intense emotional energy.
Provokes to return us to the flow and spirit.
39-55

Managing financial resources.
14-2

TRIBAL CIRCUIT - DEFENSE

Life Purpose Design
Body (Vehicle)

With a **red** marker, color your defined Design (unconscious) Gates and red/**black** checked Gates as shown on your Human Design Chart

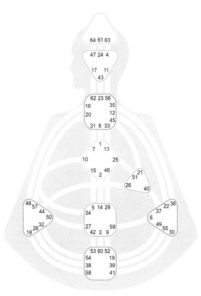

Channels:

50-27

59-6

Channel of Preservation. Nurturing 'Mama-Bear' Energy. Looks after the family and that resources are available.
Survival in the Now (Spleen Center) Yin-Energy.

General Characteristics of the Defense Circuit:

Not logical. Intense.

Aura busting energy - you are forced to comply with the rules of the tribe.

Life and death consequences.

Resources and reproduction.

Soul Purpose
Personality (Passenger)

Nurturing. Look after the family 50-27 Yin

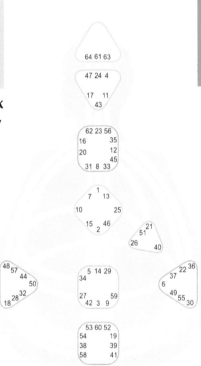

Reproduction, Protective (war) 59-6 Yang

With a **black** marker, color your defined **Personality (conscious) Gates** and red/**black** checked Gates as shown on your Human Design Chart

Channels:

50-27

59-6

Channel of Reproduction Energy for war, sex and bonding. Should wait for clarity before jumping in (Emotional Solar Plexus Center). Yang-Energy.

TRIBAL CIRCUIT - ECONOMIC

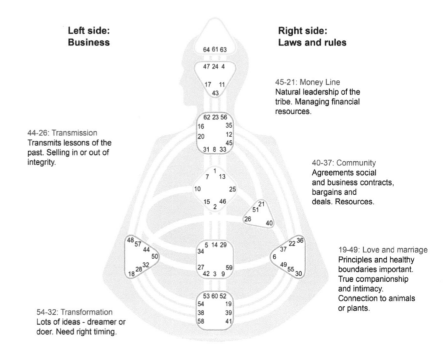

Life Purpose Design
Body (Vehicle)

Left side:
Business

Right side:
Laws and rules

45-21: Money Line
Natural leadership of the
tribe. Managing financial
resources.

44-26: Transmission
Transmits lessons of the
past. Selling in or out of
integrity.

40-37: Community
Agreements social
and business contracts,
bargains and
deals. Resources.

19-49: Love and marriage
Principles and healthy
boundaries important.
True companionship
and intimacy.
Connection to animals
or plants.

54-32: Transformation
Lots of ideas - dreamer or
doer. Need right timing.

With a **red** marker, color
your defined **Design**
(unconscious) Gates and
red/black checked Gates
as shown on your Human
Design Chart

Channels:
44-26
54-32
19-49
40-37
45-21

General Characteristics of the Ego Circuit:

Business, resources, sales, money/resource allocation and management, deals, contracts, agreements.

Marriage, divorce, social contracts. Will power.

Not generated. Ambition. Dreaming.

Two streams: Intimacy and Relationship/contracts.

19-49 Channel and 37-40 Channel

Soul Purpose
Personality (Passenger)

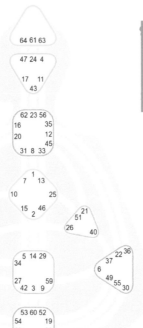

Selling with integrity
44-26

Natural Soverignity
(Leadership)
45-21

With a **black** marker, color your defined **Personality (conscious) Gates** and red/**black** checked Gates as shown on your Human Design Chart

I'll do this
if you do that
(bargain)
40-37

Dreamer with lots of ideas
when waits and trusts 54-32

Principles and healthy
boundaries.
High sensitivity. 19-49

Channels:
44-26
54-32
19-49
40-37
45-21

COLLECTIVE CIRCUIT – PATTERN (Logic)
Life Purpose Design
Body (Vehicle)

With a red marker, color your defined **Design (unconscious) Gates** and red/**black** checked Gates as shown on your Human Design Chart

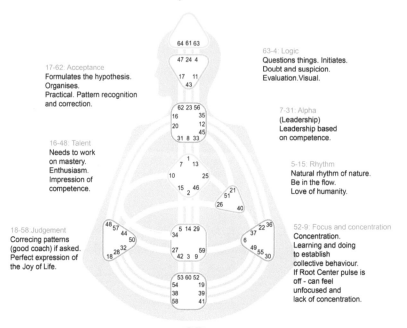

17-62: Acceptance
Formulates the hypothesis.
Organises.
Practical. Pattern recognition and correction.

16-48: Talent
Needs to work on mastery.
Enthusiasm.
Impression of competence.

18-58:Judgement
Correcing patterns (good coach) if asked.
Perfect expression of the Joy of Life.

63-4: Logic
Questions things. Initiates.
Doubt and suspicion.
Evaluation.Visual.

7-31: Alpha
(Leadership)
Leadership based on competence.

5-15: Rhythm
Natural rhythm of nature.
Be in the flow.
Love of humanity.

52-9: Focus and concentration
Concentration.
Learning and doing to establish collective behaviour.
If Root Center pulse is off - can feel unfocused and lack of concentration.

Channels:

63-4
17-62
16-48
18-58
52-9
5-15
7-31

General Characteristics of the
Understanding (Logic) Circuit:

Learn best through repetition.

All about patterns that repeat over time (finding, establishing them, etc.) i.e. Spring comes each year after winter.

Look at patterns of the past to bring ideas into the future. (great for research, scientific projects). All theory, hypothetical - with the Channel 52-9 comes the doing and aligning and integration into patterns of the natural world and life force.

Infrastructure that protects the collective and for the greater good of humanity.

Left: logic, numbers

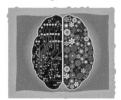

Soul Purpose
Personality (Passenger)

Highly visual

Right eye   **Left Brain**

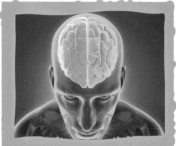

Enthusiasm and depth
16-48

```
        64 61 63

        47 24  4

         17   11
            43


        62 23 56
      16         35
      20         12
                 45
        31  8 33


          1
        7   13

      10        25

        15   46
          2
             21
           51
        26     40


    48 57       5 14 29      22 36
       44     34          37
         50              6
    28 32     27     59   49 55
   18         42 3  9        30


        53 60 52
      54         19
      38         39
      58         41
```

Doubt, suspicion
63-4

Opinions and Details.
Practical. 17-62

With a **black** marker, color
your defined **Personality**
(conscious) Gates and
red/**black** checked Gates
as shown on your Human
Design Chart

Channels:

63-4
17-62
16-48
18-58
52-9
5-15
7-31

Supported
(democratic)
Leadership
7-31

Attuned to Natural
rhythms of nature
5-15

Corrects patterns
18-58

Focussed concentration
9-52

A Step by Step Interactive Guidebook Based on Your Human Design Chart – 131

COLLECTIVE CIRCUIT – MIRACLE (Abstract)

Life Purpose Design
Body (Vehicle)

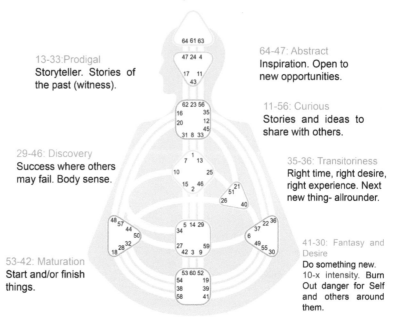

With a **red** marker, color your defined **Design (unconscious) Gates** and **red**/**black** checked Gates as shown on your Human Design Chart

13-33:Prodigal
Storyteller. Stories of the past (witness).

64-47: Abstract
Inspiration. Open to new opportunities.

11-56: Curious
Stories and ideas to share with others.

29-46: Discovery
Success where others may fail. Body sense.

35-36: Transitoriness
Right time, right desire, right experience. Next new thing- allrounder.

53-42: Maturation
Start and/or finish things.

41-30: Fantasy and Desire
Do something new. 10-x intensity. Burn Out danger for Self and others around them.

Channels:

64-47
11-56
13-33
35-36
29-46
41-30
53-42

General Characteristics of the
Sensing (Abstract) Circuit:

Get it after one time - Do NOT need repetition!

Conventional schooling (logic-repetition) is not suitable. Difficult to exist in a predominantly logical culture.

Use their five senses to help with learning. Learn in their own way. Need integrative experiences - maybe even background music.

Answers are available, but often inexplicable how they got them. (A-ha! experiences). Strengths and talents need to be nurtured. Need emotional stability to learn.

Soul Purpose
Personality (Passenger)

Right Brain   Left eye

Highly visual

Right brain: Creativity

Confusion, putting
data into some order
to make sense.
Inspiration.
64-47

64 61 63

47 24 4

17 11
43

Lots of ideas, good
storyteller (teacher).
11-56

62 23 56
16   35
20   12
         45
31 8 33

With a **black** marker, color
your defined **Personality
(conscious) Gates** and
red/**black** checked Gates
as shown on your Human
Design Chart

Listening and sharing.
Keep secrets - or not.
13-33

1
7   13
10   25
15 46
2

21
51
26   40

Channels:

64-47
11-56
13-33
35-36
29-46
41-30
53-42

Jack of all Trades
(allrounder).
Gets bored easily.
35-36

Commitments
and physical body
29-46

48 57
44
50
28 32
18

5 14 29
34

27   59
42 3 9

22 36
37
6
49 55
30

Enegy to start and finish
things 53 - 42

53 60 52
54   19
38   39
58   41

10x intensity. Visionary.
41-30

Right timing, learning, and integration are determined
by the Emotional Solar Plexus Center (emotional
wave).

CIRCUITS, CHANNELS, and KEYNOTES

Channel / Circuit: **Keynote:**

INTEGRATION

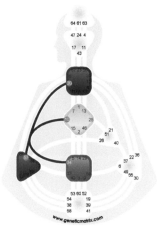

10-20 Awakening (Self-Assurance)

20-34 Charisma (Responsive Power)

10-57 Perfected Form (Human Potential)

34-57 Power (Hearing)

20-57 Brainwave (Prediction)

'Buddha Channel' (higher principles)

Busy doing - thoughts must become deeds

Intuitive survival in the NOW

Intuitive Lifeforce

Awareness in the Now.

Brings the right people and talents intuitively together.

Also part of the Knowing Circuit.

INDIVIDUAL CIRCUIT
KNOWING

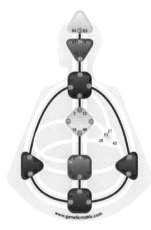

61-24 Awareness (Cosmic Perspective)

43-23 Structuring (Innovative Thinking)

38-28 Struggle (Meaning)

57-20 Brainwave (Prediction)

3-60 Mutation (Innovation)

Lost in their own thoughts; thinker

Thoughts to words (Freak or Genius)

Worth fighting for

Awareness in the Now
Brings the right people and talents intuitively together
Also part of the Integration Circuit

Brings change to the world

Channel / Circuit:	Keynote:
INDIVIDUAL CIRCUIT	
Gnostic (continued)	

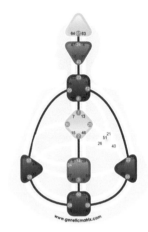

14-2 Beat (Progress)

Keeper of the Keys
Generates and manages (financial) resources

1-8 Inspiration (Self-Fulfillment)

39-55 Emoting (Deliberate Creation)

12-22 Openness (Grace)

Creative Role Model
Creative contribution to the world

Moodiness; cylces of creativity

Speaking from the right mood
(S-plexus energy)

Centering

10-34 Exploration (Courage)

Empowered through BEing and reacting Follow own convictions

25-51 Initiation (Higher Purpose)

Initiation/shock back to Spirit

Channel / Circuit:

**TRIBAL CIRCUIT
DEFENSE**

Keynote:

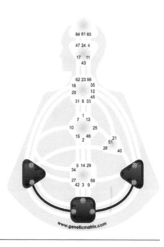

50-27 Preservation (Sustenance)

59-6 Reproduction (Provision)

Nurture, Values, Education. Protec
and sustain the Tribe.

Resources, sex, war.

Ego (*Business = left side of Ego Circuit)

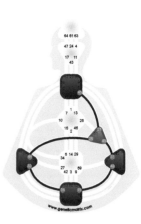

32-54* Transformation (Revelation)

Business dream of the workaholic;
feels driven

26-44* Surrender (Alignment)

Transmits lessons from the past; sales

19-49 Love and marriage (Intimacy &
Connection)

Upholding intimate, emotional
contracts

40-37 Community (Administration)

Principles + boundaries important;
connection animals

21-45 Materialism (Sustainable
Resources)

Agreements and contracts; resources

Lead the tribe, abundant resources;
materialist

CIRCUITS, CHANNELS, and KEYNOTES

Channel / Circuit:

Keynote:

COLLECTIVE CIRCUIT
UNDERSTANDING (LOGIC)

63-4   Logic   (Potentiality)

Create a hypothesis, doubts; visual

17-62 Acceptance (Formulation)

Organizing, practical

16-48 Wavelength/Talent (Mastery)

Enthusiastic, impression of competence (talent)

18-58 Judgement (Improvement)

Perfect expression of the joy of life

9-52   Focus and concentration (Clarity)

Learn and do - to establish collective behavior

5-15   Rhythm (Natural Order)

Natural rhythms of nature; love of humanity; being in the flow

7-31   Alpha/Leader (Egalitarianism)

Natural leadership based on competence

CIRCUITS, CHANNELS, and KEYNOTES

Channel / Circuit:	Keynote:
Sensing (Abstract)	
64-47 Absstraction (Divine Potential)	Inspiration; confusion - make sense out of all the data
11-56 Curiosity (Framework)	Seeker; stories and ideas about life to share with others
42-53 Maturation (Executive Function)	Start and/or finish things
59-46 Discovery (Dedication)	Success where others fail; body sense
13-33 The Prodigal (Collective Consciousness)	Storyteller, stories of the past; witness
41-30 Fantasy and Desire/Recognition (Intention)	Do something new; 10x Intensity - burn out self and others
36-35 Transitoriness (Threshold)	Right time, right desire, right experience; next new thing.

Section Eight
Planets

GATES and PLANETS

IN HUMAN DESIGN, EACH PLANET HAS A PARTICULAR THEME. THE GATES SHOW WHICH THEMES **are activated.**

On the Human Design Chart, the symbols of the planets are shown with the Gates and the lines:

Sun	☉ 8.6 / ☉ 29.4
Earth	⊕ 14.6 / ⊕ 30.4
North Node	☊ 35.3 / ☊ 16.6
South Node	☋ 5.3 / ☋ 9.6
Moon	☽ 60.1 / ☽ 20.4
Mercury	☿ 27.6 / ☿ 4.1
Venus	♀ 16.4 / ♀ 46.4
Mars	♂ 64.3 / ♂ 50.4
Jupiter	♃ 16.1 / ♃ 12.4
Saturn	♄ 63.5 / ♄ 63.4
Uranus	♅ 40.6 / ♅ 64.3
Neptune	♆ 1.6 / ♆ 1.5
Pluto	♇ 64.3 / ♇ 64.5
Chiron	⚷ 64.3 / ⚷ 64.5

GOOD TO KNOW

Planet Chiron (⚷) is sometimes shown, but it is never filled in as part of the Human Design Chart definition like the other Gates. Chiron is shown for informational purposes only as it plays a role when looking at life cycles.

FUNNEL DIAGRAM

IMAGINE ALL THE PLANETARY ENERGIES, AND THE NEUTRINOS ARE PUSHED INTO A BIG FUNNEL. At the other end, 70% of all that information that goes through the funnel actually is Sun and Earth energy. This is why the themes of your Sun and Earth energy (also called your incarnation cross) are so dominant and important in your life.

All Planetary Energies into the funnel:

Sun, Earth, Moon, Nodes, Mercury, Venus, Mars, Jupiter, Saturn, Uranus, Neptune, Pluto, Chiron, Neutrino Stream, etc.

70% = Sun and Earth Energy
(Incarnation Cross)

Dominates our Life Themes and tells us our Life Story.

INCARNATION CROSS

SUN AND EARTH GATE POSITIONS ARE ALWAYS OPPOSITE ONE OTHER ON THE HUMAN DESIGN Mandala. The Gates of the Sun and Earth define the Incarnation Cross, which is usually shown on the Human Design Chart.

The energies of the Sun and Earth represent 70% of the energy in the Human Design Chart (the theme of our experiences in this life).

 **Earth is the receptive energy in the Chart (Yin-Energy).**

 **The Sun represents what we push out or express in the world (Yang-Energy).**

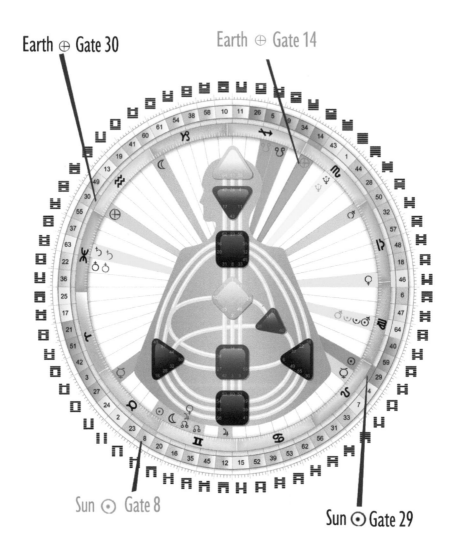

Earth ⊕ Gate 30

Earth ⊕ Gate 14

Sun ⊙ Gate 8

Sun ⊙ Gate 29

Look at your **HUMAN DESIGN CHART** and write down the **GATE** numbers that are written next to the **SUN** ☉ and **EARTH** ⊕:

LIFE PURPOSE (Design)

My unconscious Sun q is in:

GATE: _____

CIRCUIT: _____

The meaning (theme) of this **GATE** is:

_____

_____

_____

My unconscious Earth a is in:

GATE:_____

CIRCUIT:_____

The meaning (theme) of this **GATE** is:

_____

_____

_____

SOUL PURPOSE (Personality)

My conscious Sun ☉ is in:

GATE: _____

CIRCUIT: _____

The meaning (theme) of this **GATE** is:

_____

_____

_____

My conscious Earth a is in:

GATE: _____

CIRCUIT: _____

The meaning (theme) of this **GATE** is:

_____

_____

_____

My INCARNATION CROSS is (Look at your CHART):

_____

MEANING of the PLANETS (HUMAN DESIGN)

THE ENERGY OF THE SUN AND EARTH IS 70% OF YOUR CHART AND SHOW WHAT THEMES YOU have in this life.

The signs on the Chart are the symbols for the planets, which come from astrology. The planets bring the lessons and opportunities to step fully into our authentic expression so we can get clear and leave our legacy.

Each planet moves at its own speed and takes varying times to complete a cycle and circle the Human Design Mandala, passing through all the gates.

The planets move at different speeds around the sun. Generally speaking the planets can be put into 3 categories:

1. **Personal influence:** The inner planets – Sun, Moon, Mercury, Venus and Mars – move quickly through the Gates.

2. **Our relationship to society:** Jupiter and Saturn – take longer to move through the Gates.

3. **Generational influence:** The outer planets – Uranus, Neptune and Pluto – take quite long to move through the Gates.

One sign of the zodiac = 8 Human Design Gates (hexagrams)

Here is a list of how long each planet takes to transit a zodiac (astrological) sign:

Sun: 30 days

Moon: 2.5 days

Mercury: 14-20 days

Venus: 23 days to 2 months

Mars: 1.5 months

Jupiter: 1 year

Saturn: 2.5 years

Uranus: 7 years

Neptune: 14 years

Pluto: 14-30 years

Chiron: 1.5 – 8 years   (This could also be placed under the individual planet)

Healing opportunities are also always provided so we can do what we came here to do.

Symbol/Planet	Meaning	Timing
Sun **Astrology:** Rules Leo	This is the most important energy in the Chart. The Sun shows what you push out (express) into the world. Yang/masculine energy quality.	 365 Days
Earth 	Earth energy grounds you and shows you where you receive energy, as well as how it influences your experiences in the world. Yin/feminine energy quality.	 365 Days

Symbol/Planet	Meaning	Timing

 Moon

The Moon shows the driving force in your life and what archetype you are driven to live.
It shows what emotional security you need and where to retreat to feel secure.

28 Days

Astrology: Rules Cancer

♋ **North Node**

Nodes are the themes of a person's life. The energies can be felt for a yang lifetime, but are more noticeable at different ages and with different emphasis at different times in the life cycle.

38-42 Years

- *Youth – maturity (40 years+) phase.* What are you here to move towards? What you express past midlife as your wisdom.
- *40 years+, 2nd half of life cycle - 'breathing out' yang phase.*

Life Cycle to monitor: **Age 38-42+/-** Uranus Opposition. When Uranus opposition is in the position it was at birth, this flips from the south to the north node theme.

Symbol/Planet	Meaning	Timing

☋ South Node

Birth to 40 years, 1st half life cycle - 'breathing in' phase. What you receive or 'take in' (yin) in your youth.

What you've mastered in the past, before the age of 40.

The nodes are not so relevant for 6th line profiles as Chiron flips and is the stronger influence. (4/6, 3/6, 6/3, 6/2 profiles).

It is vital to look at the Uranus opposition reading for all profiles except the 6th line, as they are not deeply affected by Uranus.

38-42 Years

☿ Mercury

Shows how you are here to communicate and share with the world.

The Gate shows what you are here to talk about/ message to share.

1 Year

Retrograde 3x/year for 3 Weeks

Astrology: Rules Gemini.
(and previously Virgo - now Chiron is ruling planet).

Symbol/Planet	Meaning	Timing

 Venus

Shows what your values are in life and what you love. Also the theme in relationship with the yin energy (attracted to and lessons to learn).

Who and what do we draw to ourselves?

224 Days

Retrograde every 1 1/2 - 2 years

Astrology: Rules Libra

 Mars

Mars is a fast-moving, quick planet, and does not stay around long. Mars is the planet of immaturity and consequent maturity with experience and also the potential for growth in our youth.

Whatever is in Mars is where you will have lessons and opportunities for growth on a personal level.

It is a theme in relationships with the yang energy (attracted to and lessons to learn).

3rd or 6th lines in Mars make challenges more extreme and the potential for wisdom greater.

2 Years

Retrograde every 2 years

Astrology: Rules Aires

Symbol/Planet	Meaning	Timing

♃ Jupiter

Shows the rewards or blessings you receive when you master your Saturn challenge.

Be a source of blessings or a place for growth.

Dances with Saturn. Gifts and opportunities life brings to us.

12 Years

Astrology: Rules Saggitarius

♄ Saturn

Challenge you have in life. It is our spiritual barbed wire fence. If you are not living in alignment with your energy blueprint, then Saturn will let you know – it is the teacher (sometimes seen as the punisher). It pokes you if you are not in alignment or denying aspects of yourself.

Look at these Gates if you feel stuck. If you are in alignment, you will be rewarded and receive the blessings of Jupiter. It is a place for you to grow.

6th line profiles benefit from a Saturn return reading before they go 'up on the roof'.

Life Cycles to pay attention to: At age 28+/- and again at 58+/-

29 ½ Years

Astrology: Rules Capricorn

Symbol/Planet	Meaning	Timing

 Uranus

Slower moving planet - more a generational theme, but can also be felt personally. Change here is always radical and signifies deep transition and evolution. Whatever is here appears in unexpected and strange ways. It wakes you to different ways of being.

Is the place where you are unusual when you look at the Gate. Is where you align with others like you.

Whatever Gate is here, indicates where you might experience a lot of unique and unexpected changes. Planet of initiation and awakening.

Life Cycle to pay attention to: Age 84+/-

84 Years

Astrology: Rules Aquarius

 **Neptune**

Is your spiritual work and purpose in life. Neptune is a deeply spiritual planet and somewhat mysterious. The Gate defines the vehicle for your spiritual journey.

Neptune is a slow planet and so a generational theme. Is often the planet associated with drugs, alcohol, and addictions (especially if Gate 51 or 28 is here).

Shows where you need to remove illusion and reveal truth.

165 Years

Astrology: Rules Pisces

Symbol/Planet	Meaning	Timing

 Pluto

Represents endings and new beginnings.

High expression: expansion and growth; low expression: obsessive desire for power and control and general destructiveness. It is a purely generational theme.

The challenges of Pluto present collective, generational challenges that must be overcome in a unified way.

248 Years

Astrology: Scorpio

 **Chiron (Kiron)**

Shows your life's spiritual purpose if born after 1978. This planet is not shown on all Human Design Charts.

6th line profiles benefit from a Chiron return reading (around 50 years of age) when they come 'off the roof'.

If you don't master the lessons of Chiron at around age 50, then you have to deal with the same theme through Saturn around end 50/beginning 60 years of age.

For those born after 1978 (when Chiron was discovered), this theme is already integrated into the whole Chart, so it is not such a challenging theme anymore around age 50.

Life Cycle to pay attention to: Age 50+/- if born before 1978 (when Chiron was discovered).

50 Years

Astrology rules : Virgo.

Finding your Life Purpose

Look at the meaning of the Gates in the following planets as shown on your **Human Design Chart.**

Chiron:
Spiritual
Purpose

Chiron shows where we have our healing powers as the result of our own spiritual wounds.

For 6th line profiles Chiron indicates the leadership role they will play after their Chiron return.

For the others it indicates the spiritual challenges that must be mastered to live out your destiny.

Earth:
Receptive

Incarnation Cross: (Sun + Earth) What you are here to do.
Themes of the Incarnation Cross can only be lived out when you are living in alignment with your energy blueprint (Design).

Moon:
Driving Force

The moon tells you the 'why' behind your Incarnation Cros

Is what drives you.

Neptune:
Spiritual Destiny

Neptune can be unclear and murky especially if you are not following your strategy and living in alignment with your energ blueprint (Design).

Saturn:
Teacher

Saturn shows the bigger theme, can be your best teacher, or it can feel like punishment. You have to live your strategy according to Typ otherwise you will be 'punished' in whatever gate is shown in Satur Brings big gifts and blessings when the challenges are mastered.

Jupiter:
Spiritual Blessing

Jupiter is the planet of expansion and blessings so long as you live your

strategy according to Type and master the challenges of Saturn.

Above you can write down the Gates (black/red) that are next to the planets on your Human Design Chart.

MY LIFE STORY

I _____(name), powerfully and passionately declare that my Life Purpose is

(Sun q - Personality Gate theme) _____and

(Sun q - Design Gate theme) _____.

To do this I allow, create and receive

(Earth a - Personality theme) _____and

(Earth a - Design Gate theme) _____

as part of the foundation of the deep well of creativity that I AM.

My heart and soul are driven by

(Moon N- Personality Gate theme) _____and

(Moon N - Design Gate theme) _____.

I know that nurturing this drive gives me the energy and passion to continue to align myself with my purpose.

I embrace the challenge as part of my learning and growth process. I know that when I encounter an inner conflict that this is a symptom of my own expansion and indicates that I am learning and growing. I am always doing it right. I am always growing and changing.

My personal learning energy teaches me

(Saturn r – Personality Gate theme) _____ and

(Saturn r- Design Gate theme) _____.

MY LIFE STORY

When I master my inner lessons, I am blessed by

(Jupiter c- Personality Gate theme) _____ and

(Jupiter c- Design Gate theme) _____.

My Spiritual Purpose and Path is

(Neptune v - Personality Gate theme) _____and

(Neptune v- Design Gate theme) _____.

I call on these energies when I am in need of greater alignment with my Purpose.

I know that I need to master

(Chiron g - Personality Gate theme) _____and

(Chiron g - Design Gate theme) _____

to deepen what I am here to share with the world.

I use this knowledge and wisdom to communicate through

(Mercury x - Personality Gate theme) _____and

(Mercury x – Design Gate theme) _____.

I share the full expression of who I am with the world through these energies.

I play a unique role in the evolution of Humanity and I have a vital and irreplaceable place in Divine Order.

I honor all of who I am and I deeply and completely love and accept myself.

(Used with Permission: © Karen Curry Parker, Creator of The Quantum Alignment System, LLC)

Section Nine

Completing the Story

BE TRUE TO YOU

I ONCE READ AN EXPLANATION WHY THE LAW OF ATTRACTION DOES NOT ALWAYS WORK - PARAPHRASING here, it said that the techniques don't work when you are not in alignment with who you really are and what you really want as well as need. You have to be true to yourself.

This illustrates why, in my opinion, Human Design is an important tool that everyone should know.

Here are a few questions that you can ask yourself:
- What if I am already perfect, the way I am?
- How would I feel and what would I do?
- What would I have?
- Who could I be?
- How would things change?

Abundance, belief, and trust are the way to lead us away from the feeling of lack and fear. Even if this material is too much to process and take in at the moment, the most important takeaway in Human Design is to:

FOLLOW YOUR STRATEGY ACCORDING TO YOUR TYPE.

PLEASE STAY OPEN AND TRUST
THAT OPPORTUNITIES WILL ALWAYS ARISE

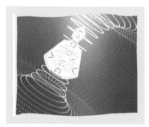

Use your head to ask questions and leave it to the Universe to bring you the answers. The head is not designed to find solutions.

Please practice self-care. If you are burned out, then you will not be able to attract the correct things for you into your life. If you are tired, you need a period of rest so that your Magnetic Monopole can work in your best interests.

The best contribution you can give to this world is just to BE YOURSELF and follow your joy (you do *not* have to do anything).

My teacher always reminds us students of the following:

> We are all designed to be abundant, happy, have meaning as well as direction in our lives that fulfill us and make us valuable, empowering, loving, and compassionate Beings.

> Remember YOU are a unique once-in-a-lifetime event and have an important role in this Universe. We are because YOU are. YOU ARE UNIQUE, worthy, and lovable – an unbelievable blessing for the World.

> Everyone - including YOU - has an important part to play in the big puzzle of life. (*Quoted from Karen Curry Parker*).

Just BE YOURSELF and share your talents with the world.
YOU are UNIQUE.

Suggested Resources

Here is a list of some of the resources I like to use.
Please also do your own research, as this list is only a small selection of the vast amount of information available.

For books and products related to Human Design
www.humandesignstore.com

www. quantumalignmentsystem.com
(helpful videos, info and listing of practitioners trained by Karen Curry Parker)

www.freehumandesignchart.com (free Chart and info on your Type)

Free charts:
www.freehumandesignchart.com
www.geneticmatrix.com
www.newsunware.com

Books:
Introduction to Quantum Human Design (and other books) by Karen Curry Parker
Understanding your Clients through Human Design by Robin Winn
Getting to know You by Karen Flaherty
The Human Design Reflector by Amber Clements
The Definitive Book of Human Design by Lynda Bunnell and Ra Uru Hu
The Human Design Ephemeris (Planetary Transits) by Zen Human Design (humandesign.com)
Books by Chetan Parkyn

Rosy Aronson:
The Wisdom Keepers (book and Cards - Art and text based on Human Design)
www.rosyaronson.com
www.designedtoblossom.com

Karen Flaherty:
Getting to know YOU (book) www.livingbyhumandesign.com

Closing Comments

AS A STUDENT OF HUMAN DESIGN, I STARTED TO FEEL A BIT OVERWHELMED WITH ALL THE INFORMATION AND material available on the topic. I wanted to understand what my Chart meant but couldn't find all the information I wanted in one place and didn't really know what information would help me. I didn't know how to go about putting the pieces of my Chart together. In addition, having undefined Head and Anja Centers made it difficult for to me recall the information I read, so I created this book to help others understand the basics of Human Design.

I find visual images and color codes help me a lot to learn - so that is also how I have designed this book. It is a bit like a reference manual. You can return and refer to pages; it also has empty Chart diagrams for you to color in yourself with some questions on your Chart, to help you better see and grasp your own unique energetic design. The information is in keynote style with images and gives a basic overview of what's in your Human Design Chart.

My goal is to provide practical information that the majority can understand. I consider this book as foundational material to help you gain an overview of Human Design and whether you want to dive deeper into the topic. For those of you just starting to learn Human Design, there might be too much information or not enough detail, but I hope this book helps you to understand the basics. For those of you that already know Human Design, I believe that this might be a good reference book as it also helps in explaining the concepts to others.

My aim is to help Human Design become more well known so that many more know their Type and Strategy in order to optimize how they interact with others and have a way of getting to know their energy better.

I would like to express my gratitude and appreciation to Karen Curry Parker, founder of Quantum Alignment Systems LLC, for being such a heart-centered, encouraging, supportive, and motivating teacher. I also want to thank the GracePoint Matrix team for their assistance and professional support in producing this book.

Publishing Page

Find more Human Design books and guides like this
one from GracePoint Publishing.
https://gracepointpublishing.com/bookstore/

About the Author

DENISE IS A TRAINED HUMAN DESIGN SPECIALIST WITH A DESIRE TO HELP MAKE HUMAN DESIGN MORE WELL-KNOWN TO A WIDER AUDIENCE. SHE USED TO WORK IN THE BANKING SECTOR AND HAS ALWAYS BEEN INTERESTED IN TOPICS TO DO WITH ENERGY AND SELF-HEALING. AS A PROJECTOR, LEARNING HUMAN DESIGN HAS HELPED HER TO BETTER UNDERSTAND, APPRECIATE AND LOOK AFTER HER ENERGY

CPSIA information can be obtained
at www.ICGtesting.com
Printed in the USA
BVHW021725081121
621068BV00002B/23